Managing Reality

Book One
Introduction to the Engineering and Construction Contract

Second edition

Managing Reality

Book One
Introduction to the Engineering and Construction Contract

Second edition

Bronwyn Mitchell and Barry Trebes

Published by ICE Publishing, 40 Marsh Wall, London E14 9TP.

Full details of ICE Publishing sales representatives and distributors can be found at:
www.icevirtuallibrary.com/printbooksales

First edition published 2005

Also available in this series from ICE Publishing Books
Managing Reality, Book Two: Procuring an Engineering and Construction Contract, Second edition.
ISBN 978-0-7277-5720-3
Managing Reality, Book Three: Managing the Contract, Second edition. ISBN 978-0-7277-5722-7
Managing Reality, Book Four: Managing Change, Second edition. ISBN 978-0-7277-5724-1
Managing Reality, Book Five: Managing Procedures, Second edition. ISBN 978-0-7277-5726-5

A catalogue record for this book is available from the British Library

9 8 7 6 5 4 3 2 1

ISBN 978-0-7277-5718-0

© Thomas Telford Limited 2012

ICE Publishing is a division of Thomas Telford Ltd, a wholly-owned subsidiary of the Institution of
Civil Engineers (ICE).

Typeset by Academic + Technical, Bristol
Printed and bound by CPI Group (UK) Ltd, Croydon CR0 4YY

Contents

Preface

In the preface to the first edition of *Managing Reality*, in 2005, we set out our aims and aspirations for 'Managing Reality'. These were as follows.

- To add and contribute to the body of knowledge on the use of the NEC ECC.
- To provide a book which focuses on the 'how to': how to manage and administer the ECC contract.
- To present as a five-part book-set that covers both the needs of the student professional or prospective client, through to the novice practitioner and experienced user.
- To provide a rounded view of the ECC, whatever your discipline, on both sides of the contractual relationship
- To enable everyone to realise the business benefits from using the NEC suite of contracts generally and the ECC in particular.
- *Managing Reality* does not attempt to give a legal treatise or a blow-by-blow review of each and every clause. It is intended to be complementary to other publications, which give excellent theoretical and legal perspectives.

This book is about dealing with the reality of real life projects: Managing Reality.

The feedback and support we have received since its first publication in 2005 has been universally positive and we would like to thank all of you who have bought and used *Managing Reality* since its first publication.

We have greatly enjoyed updating and working on this second edition and we hope that it continues to provide a useful body of knowledge on the use of the NEC3 ECC.

Bronwyn Mitchell and Barry Trebes

Foreword

A key objective of the first edition of *Managing Reality* was to provide a five-part book to meet the needs of students, prospective clients, novice practitioners and experienced users. Satisfying such diverse needs is an ambitious objective for any text.

Does *Managing Reality* achieve its stated aim? I believe that the answer to this is a resounding 'yes'. In my view, the calibre of authorship is exceptional. All levels of and types of readership from the uninitiated to the experienced professional will derive considerable benefit from this text. Although written in a very accessible style, there is no skimping on detail or on addressing difficult issues. The worked examples are particularly helpful. *Managing Reality* should be your prime aid from the moment you are considering whether or not to use an NEC contract right through to using and operating the contract.

But *Managing Reality* is much more than simply a 'how to' guide. It seeks to deliver a clear message that NEC contracts cannot be used to their full potential unless one is prepared to ditch one's knowledge and experience of traditional contracting. For example, emphasis is placed on the fact that certainty and predictability are the hallmarks of NEC contracts. Open-ended and subjective phrases and concepts have no place in NEC contracting.

I am privileged to be associated with this second edition of *Managing Reality*. It will continue to help those who need help overcoming any reservations about using NEC contracts and re-inforce existing users in their continued use of these ground-breaking contracts.

Professor Rudi Klein
President, NEC Users' Group

Acknowledgements

We would like to thank the following individuals and companies who have supported the book.

For their active participation in this book we would like to thank

- Professor Rudi Klein (SEC Group Chief Executive) for writing the Foreword
- Dr Robert N. Hunter of Hunter and Edgar Edinburgh for his thoughts and suggested revisions for this second edition
- Gavin Jamieson, the Senior Commissioning Editor, for his enthusiasm and patience
- colleagues at Mott MacDonald
- everyone who has given feedback on the book since 2005.

And our continued gratitude to those who provided support and input into the first edition of *Managing Reality*.

- Mike Attridge, of Ellenbrook Consulting, who reviewed the book on behalf of the authors.
- David H. Williams who provided guidance and support in the development of the book.
- Everyone at Needlemans Limited Construction Consultants (now part of the Mott MacDonald Group).
- Everyone at MPS Limited with whom Needlemans Limited worked to develop the first web based management system for the NEC in 2000.

Finally, we would like to thank our family and friends for their on-going support, understanding and patience.

Series contents

The following outlines the content of the five books in the series.

List of figures

List of tables

Introduction to the Engineering and Construction Contract
ISBN 978-0-7277-5718-0

Introduction

General

This series of books will provide the people who are actually using the Engineering and Construction Contract (ECC) in particular, and the New Engineering Contract (NEC) suite in general, practical guidance as to how to prepare and manage an ECC contract with confidence and knowledge of the effects of their actions on the Contract and the other parties.

Each book in the series addresses a different area of the management of an ECC contract.

- Book One – Managing Reality: Introduction to the Engineering and Construction Contract.
- Book Two – Managing Reality: Procuring an Engineering and Construction Contract.
- Book Three – Managing Reality: Managing the Contract.
- Book Four – Managing Reality: Managing Change.
- Book Five – Managing Reality: Managing Procedures.

- *Book One (Managing Reality: Introduction to the Engineering and Construction Contract)* is for those who are considering using the ECC but need further information, or those who are already using the ECC but need further insight into its rationale. It therefore focuses on the fundamental cultural changes and mind-shift that are required to successfully manage the practicalities of the ECC in use.

- *Book Two (Managing Reality: Procuring an Engineering and Construction Contract)* is for those who need to know how to procure an ECC contract. It covers in practical detail the invitations to tender, evaluation of submissions, which option to select, how to complete the Contract Data and how to prepare the Works Information. The use of this guidance is appropriate for employers, contractors (including subcontractors) and construction professionals generally.

- *Book Three (Managing Reality: Managing the Contract)* is essentially for those who use the contract on a daily basis, covering the detail of practical management such as paying the contractor, reviewing the programme, ensuring the quality of the works, and dispute resolution. Both first-time and experienced practitioners will benefit from this book.

- *Book Four (Managing Reality: Managing Change)* is for those who are managing change under the contract; whether for the employer or the contractor (or subcontractor), the management of change is often a major challenge whatever the form of contract. The ECC deals with change in a different way to other more traditional forms. This book sets out the steps to efficiently and effectively manage change, bridging the gap between theory and practice.

- *Book Five (Managing Reality: Managing Procedures)* gives step-by-step guidance on how to apply the most commonly used procedures, detailing the actions needed by all parties to comply with the contract. Anyone administering the contract will benefit from this book.

Background

The ECC is the first of what could be termed a 'modern contract' in that it seeks to holistically align the setting up of a contract to match business needs as opposed to writing a contract that merely administers construction events.

The whole ethos of the ECC, or indeed the NEC suite generally, is one of simplicity of language and clarity of requirement. It is important that the roles and responsibilities are equally clear in definition and ownership.

When looking at the ECC for the first time it is very easy to believe that it is relatively straightforward and simple. However, this apparent simplicity belies the need for the people involved to think about their project and their role, and how the ECC can deliver their particular contract strategy.

The ECC provides a structured flexible framework for setting up an appropriate form of contract whatever the selected procurement route. The fundamental requirements are as follows.

- The Works Information – quality and completeness – what are you asking the Contractor to do?
- The Site Information – what are the site conditions the Contractor will find?
- The Contract Data – key objectives for completion, for example, start date, completion date, programme – when do you want it completed?

The details contained in the series of books will underline the relevance and importance of the above three fundamental requirements.

The structure of the books

Each chapter starts with a synopsis of what is included in that chapter. Throughout the book there are shaded 'practical tip' boxes that immediately point the user towards important reminders for using the ECC (see example below).

> Clarity and completeness of the Works Information is fundamental.

There are also unshaded boxes that contain examples to illustrate the text (see example below).

> Imagine a situation in which the *Supervisor* notifies the *Contractor* that the reinstatement of carriageways on a utility diversion project is not to the highway authority's usual standards. However, the Works Information is silent about the reinstatement.
>
> Although it is not to the authority's usual standard, it is **not** a Defect because the test of a Defect is non-conformance with the Works Information. In this situation, if the *works* need to be redone to meet the authority's requirements, the *Contractor* is entitled to a compensation event because the new requirements are a change to the Works Information.

Other diagrams and tables are designed to maintain interest and provide another medium of explanation. There are also standard forms for use in the administration and management of the contract, together with examples.

Throughout the books, the following terms have been used in a specific way.

- NEC is the abbreviation for the suite of New Engineering Contracts and it is not the name of any single contract.
- ECC is the abbreviation for the contract in the NEC suite called the Engineering and Construction Contract.

The NEC suite currently comprises the

- Engineering and Construction Contract
- Engineering and Construction Subcontract
- Engineering and Construction Short Contract
- Engineering and Construction Short Subcontract
- Professional Services Contract
- Adjudicator's Contract
- Term Service Contract
- Term Services Short Contract
- Supply Contract
- Supply Short Contract
- Framework Contract.

Introduction to the Engineering and Construction Contract
ISBN 978-0-7277-5718-0

ICE Publishing: All rights reserved
doi: 10.1680/iecc.57180.005

Chapter 1

Introduction to the Engineering and Construction Contract, concepts and terminology

Synopsis

This chapter looks at

- an introduction to the ECC
- an identification of some of the differences between the ECC and other contracts
- an outline of the key features of the ECC
- conventions of the ECC
- concepts on which the ECC is based
- terminology used in the ECC
- terminology not used in the ECC
- how the ECC affects the way you work.

1.1 Introduction

In the past, construction employers have become increasingly dissatisfied with the construction industry because of the increased incidence of disputes and claims and the seeming inability of traditional contract forms to provide certainty of cost, time and quality.

Employers simply require greater certainty of outcome. Many employers and organisations have sought to improve this situation by

- heavily amending traditional contracts
- initiating their own forms of contract
- creating 'bespoke' contracts (normally imposing unilateral and onerous terms and conditions)
- in many instances, continuing to use older versions of traditional contracts.

This has often led to inappropriate allocation of risk between the parties. It seems clear that a change is required.

Figure 1.1 sets out some of the issues surrounding the case for change.

The Institution of Civil Engineers was the first body to react to the challenge laid down by employers. The NEC3 Engineering and Construction Contract (ECC) was developed as an improvement to the failure of the traditional forms of contract to

- deliver 'certainty of outcome' for all parties involved and
- reduce the increasing trend towards adversarial relationships, which these contracts were seemingly encouraging.

Figure 1.1 The case for change

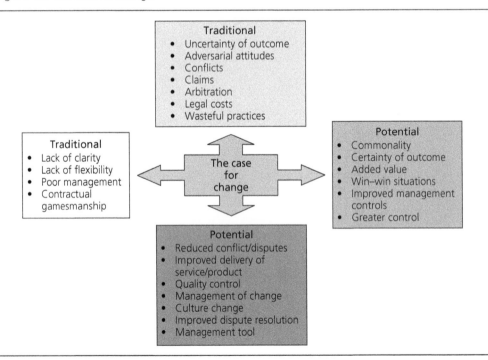

1.2 What is the ECC?

The Engineering and Construction Contract is one of a family of New Engineering Contract documents. It was published in consultative edition in 1991. The first edition was published in March 1993. In July 1994, Sir Michael Latham produced his report *Constructing the Team* in which he suggested that the New Engineering Contract complied with most of the principles for what he termed a Modern Contract and that it should be entirely appropriate for wide use.

Following the publication of the Latham report, the Institution of Civil Engineers brought forward the publication of the second edition of the New Engineering Contract (retitled

The Engineering and Construction Contract to avoid any misconceptions that it was only suited to engineering projects). The second edition published in November 1995 (a second edition was published in June 1995; however, this was withdrawn) included a number of small refinements to the first edition prompted by comment and feedback from projects on which the first edition had been used. It also included the changes recommended in the Latham Report.

The third edition was published in June 2005 and the inside cover of this edition has a statement outlining the OGC (Office of Government Commerce) endorsement of NEC3. The statement reads as follows

> '*OGC endorsement of NEC3*
> OGC advises public sector procurers that the form of contract used has to be selected according to the objectives of the project, aiming to satisfy the Achieving Excellence in Construction (AEC) principles.
> This edition of the NEC (NEC3) complies fully with the AEC principles. OGC recommends the use of NEC3 by public sector construction procurers on their construction projects.'

The OGC outlines the objective of the Achieving Excellence in Construction (AEC) initiative to be

> 'Through the Achieving Excellence initiative, Central Government clients commit to maximise, by continuous improvement, the efficiency, effectiveness and value for money of their procurement of new works, maintenance and refurbishment.'
> (From the OGC website (www.ogc.gov.uk) 3 June 2005)

The key aspects of the AEC initiative include

- use of partnering and development of long-term relationships
- the reduction of financial and decision-making approval chains
- improved skills development and empowerment
- the adoption of performance measurement indicators, use of tools such as value and risk management and whole-life costing.

The NEC suite sits very comfortably against these objectives as indicated in Table 1.1.

Table 1.1. NEC3 compliance with OGC AEC

Key objectives OGC AEC initiative	NEC3 (suite of contracts) Compliance with OGC AEC initiative requirements
■ Use of partnering and development of long-term relationships	■ Option X12 – Partnering ■ Term Service Contract ■ Framework Contract: addition to the suite of contracts
■ Reduction of financial and decision-making approval chains	■ Roles and responsibilities within the contract support this objective
■ Improved skills development and empowerment	■ Clarity of procedures
■ Adoption of performance measurement indicators, use of tools such as value and risk management and whole-life costing	■ Option X20 – Key Performance Indicators introduced into ECC3 ■ Risk management – introduction into contract of risk reduction meetings ■ Contract Data part one identifies the matters to be considered in the Risk Register

The OGC endorsement indicates the NEC suite of contracts' pre-eminence in modern procurement thinking.

1.2.1 ICE Conditions of Contract Withdraw

In 2009, the ICE Council made a decision to solely endorse the NEC3 Suite of Contracts and on Tuesday 20 July 2009 the ICE Council made a decision to withdraw from the ICE Conditions of Contract and that the out dated editions of the ICE 5th and 6th editions would be withdraw with immediate effect.

The ICE Vice President Barry Clarke said the decision follows detailed consideration by the ICE Council.

'ICE's decision to withdraw support from the ICE conditions of contract is part of a strategic realignment of our offerings and a desire to promote what we see as a more collaborative approach to contract management which offers value for money to clients and the construction industry at large.'

1.2.2 The NEC family

The NEC family includes

- the Engineering and Construction Contract
    - Consultative edition 1991 (as the New Engineering Contract)
    - First edition 1993 (as the New Engineering Contract)
    - Second edition June 1995
    - Reprinted
    - November 1995 with amendments (not applicable to Guidance Notes or Flow Charts) 1996 (Guidance Notes and Flow Charts only)
    - Reprinted May 1998 with corrections (not applicable to Guidance Notes or Flow Charts)
    - Third Edition June 2005
    - Reprinted with amendments June 2006
    - Reprinted (twice) 2007
    - Reprinted 2008.

Other documents in the New Engineering Contract family include

- the Engineering and Construction Subcontract
    - Consultative edition 1991 (The New Engineering Subcontract)
    - First edition 1993 (The New Engineering Subcontract)
    - Second edition November 1995
    - Third edition June 2005
- the Engineering and Construction Short Contract
    - First edition July 1999
    - Second edition June 2005
    - Reprinted 2007
- the Engineering and Construction Short Subcontract
    - First edition July 2001
    - Second edition June 2005
- the Professional Services Contract
    - First edition 1994
    - Second edition June 1998 Reprints
    - Third edition June 2005
- the Adjudicator's Contract
    - First edition 1994
    - Second edition 1998
    - April 2000 – Reference NEC/Y(UK)3
    - Third edition June 2005
- the Term Service Contract
    - First edition June 2005
- the Term Service Short Contract
    - First edition September 2008

- the Supply Contract
  - First edition December 2009
- the Supply Short Contract
  - First edition December 2009
- the Framework Contract
  - First edition June 2005
- Procurement and Contract Strategies
  - First edition June 2005
  - Reprinted 2007
  - Revised edition December 2009
- Chinese Translation
  - the Engineering and Construction Contract with Guidance Notes
  - First edition October 1999.

1.3 Why is the ECC different?'

The ECC is different from traditional forms of contract in a number of ways.

1   The contract has been drafted with clear objectives to make improvements in three main areas:
    - flexibility
    - clarity and simplicity
    - stimulus to good management.
2   Assessment of change is radically different and is based upon the pre-assessment of change based on forecast costs and not tendered rates and prices. It is also a principle of this process that a *Contractor* should be neither better nor worse off for an *Employer*-driven change event occurring.
3   It requires a change of culture from those who participate in the contract.
4   It encourages trust, collaboration, and early risk identification.
5   The ECC is written in the present tense.
6   There is no nomination process for Subcontractors or suppliers.
7   The ECC describes actions that are to be taken by the parties. If the parties carry out those actions, then the rights and obligations attached to those actions are fulfilled.
8   The contract is a document of procedures. The document describes the steps to be taken in the procedure, who does them and within what time-scales. If you carry out the procedures, you fulfil your obligations under the contract. This emphasises the fact that the ECC is a working document.
9   Most importantly, the document is based on a spirit of mutual trust and cooperation. These are not just fancy buzzwords dreamt up by the authors of the ECC. It is the reality of the contract supported by the processes and procedures set out in the contract. The contract will be successful if both parties follow this obligation outlined in the first clause of the contract (clause 10.1). Trust is achieved through carrying out your actions under the contract within the time frame allocated. That is, be reliable and consistent.

To achieve these objectives the ECC introduces and uses some unfamiliar terminology and gives some unfamiliar meanings to familiar terminology from traditional contracts. There are also some concepts that may be new to first-time users of the ECC or that may not be clear to some parties already using the ECC.

1.3.1 Flexibility

1   *Multi-disciplinary*. The contract avoids using words that denote a particular engineering discipline. It can therefore be used by any disciplines, such as civil, building, process, mechanical and electrical.
2   *Design*. The ECC allows for a fully designed solution by either party or a mix of *Employer* and *Contractor* design, and uses the Works Information to state the elements of the *works* that are to be *Employer* or *Contractor* designed.
3   *Pricing*. The ECC is based on a set of common core clauses, which apply to all of the six main Options, which range from Option A fixed priced lump sum to Option E cost reimbursable and Option F the management contract option. As such, the same contract can be used whether the pricing mechanism is an *activity schedule*, a *bill of*

quantities or the Schedule of Cost Components. In some larger contracts, it is possible to choose two pricing options, as long as the boundaries of scope for the two are clearly demarcated. This concept differs from traditional suites of contracts, which have specific printed versions for each contract type.

4   *Applicability*. Because of the simple language and multi-disciplinary nature of the contract, it is being used on a worldwide basis, including in Asia, Africa and South America.

Flexibility
- Multi-disciplinary
- Design
- Pricing
- Applicability

1.3.2 Clarity and simplicity

1   *Plain English*. The ECC is written in plain English and avoids the use of 'woolly words or phrases', such as 'to the reasonable satisfaction of' and 'in the opinion of'. It recognises that the interpretations of these vague words/phrases are the very seedbed of dispute. It contains very little legalese except for the inevitable words such as 'indemnity' and 'subrogation' in the insurance section. The recognition of this objective within the NEC suite of contracts is that The Plain Language Commission, whose objectives are to encourage plain English, clarity and the use of simple language rather than legalese and long complicated sentences in documents, have certificated the Short Contract.

2   *Present tense*. The first clause of the contract (clause 10.1) places the obligation on the parties by using the word 'shall'. Thereafter, the obligation having been set, the drafting is in the present tense, avoiding repeated use of the word 'shall'. This underlines the use of the ECC as a working document.

3   *Simple structure*. The simple structure of the document allows for easy translation of the ECC into other languages and facilitates the use of other documents within the NEC family because all the documents in the NEC family have the same structure.

4   *Short sentences*. Most of the sentences written in the ECC are short. Bullet points are used in the NEC documents to facilitate understanding of longer sentences. In comparison, the longest sentence in the ICE 5th contract is around 252 words.

5   *Procedures not open-ended or conflicting*. A set of documented flow charts has been drafted to accompany and complement the ECC to ensure that the procedures do come to an end and that the logic within each procedure is complete.

6   *No cross-referencing*. There is no cross-referencing or use of phrases such as 'subject to' or 'notwithstanding' in NEC documents. This means that the document as a whole has to be understood, since clauses do interact, such as clauses 16.1, 61.5 and 63.5, which deal with early warning.

7   *No reference to law*. The ECC does not specifically stipulate the requirement to adhere to Acts of Parliament, regulations, statutes and other laws passed. It refers instead to the law of the land in Contract Data part one, thereby encompassing all regulations, Acts, etc. and both Parties are required to adhere to it.

Clarity and simplicity
- Plain English
- Present tense
- Simple structure
- Short sentences
- Procedures are not open-ended and conflicting
- No cross-referencing
- No reference to law
- Set of common clauses irrespective of the main contract option chosen
(Note: also commonality of clauses in the ECC subcontract)

Copying parts of these legal obligations into the Works Information or listing them in the Contract may give rise to conflict since: (a) the words may be copied incorrectly; (b) lack of context may alter their meaning; and (c) confusion may arise as a result of the emphasis placed on some aspects of the law, but not on others. Secondary Option X2 (Changes in the law), provides an opportunity for the *Employer* to take the risk of changes in the law. Without this secondary Option the risk lies with the *Contractor*.

1.3.3 Stimulus to good management

1 *Collaborative foresight*. Working together proactively can mitigate problems and reduce the risks inherent in construction work. The ECC encourages the parties to collaborate and to think ahead.

2 *Clear allocation of responsibility*. There is a clear division of function and responsibility that helps accountability and motivation. If an action is required to be carried out, the ECC states who is responsible for carrying out the action and the time-scale for doing so.

3 *Early warning procedure*. The early warning procedure stimulates foresight, enabling the *Project Manager* to make early rational decisions about issues which may arise and which may necessitate changes to the work. Good communications facilitate the presentation and exploration of options for dealing with problems.

4 *Detailed procedure for dealing with changes*. The ECC change process recognises that change occurs on almost every contract and that if not managed carefully this change can result in disputes and lead to uncertainty of outcome in terms of cost, time and quality. Managing change as it occurs is at the heart of the ECC.

   Prompt notification through the contractual obligation of the Parties to give each other early warning of anything which could affect cost, time or quality
   - allows the *Project Manager* to be aware of changes at a far earlier point in time
   - gives him the opportunity to consider other impacts on the project
   - gives him time to consider options and make reasoned decisions.

   The whole procedure is designed to provide greater certainty of the cost and time implications of changes.

   The ECC also has a specific provision unlike other contracts for the acceptance of Defects.

5 *Programming facility*. The programme and the management of the programme is a vital part of an ECC contract and is pivotal to change management. Many of the procedures within the contract rely on an up-to-date and realistic programme maintained by the *Contractor* that is used in joint decision-making by the *Contractor* and the *Project Manager*. The programme includes method and resource statements and is defined in some detail. The *Contractor* is motivated to keep the programme up to date by way of sanctions for failure to do so.

The contract bases time implications of change on entitlement and not need, as is the case in many of the traditional contracts.

Stimulus to good management
- Collaborative foresight
- Clear allocation of responsibility
- Early warning procedure
- Detailed procedure for dealing with change
- Programming facility

1.4 ECC structure

The ECC is structured in a way that facilitates ease of use. The concept is that there is a set of core clauses which is common to all the main Options, whether the Options lead to priced, cost-based or management contracts, or whether it is a fully *Employer*-designed or *Contractor*-designed solution. This same concept is continued through into the other NEC family of contracts.

To create a priced, cost or management contract, the user is required to select one of the main Options A to F. It is the choice of these clauses that determines whether the contract is a priced, cost-based, or management contract.

Figure 1.2 ECC contract structure

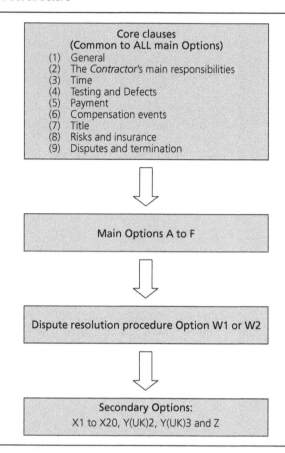

The choice of a main Option results in a useable contract; however, it is a contract that would not have retention, delay damages and the like. These are introduced by use of the secondary Option clauses. To create a more tailored Contract you require the core clauses, a main Option and then appropriate secondary Options. Figure 1.2 shows a simplistic view of the ECC contract structure.

1.5 Conventions
1.5.1 Present tense

The NEC suite of documents is written in the simple present tense rather than the simple future tense. All the actions drafted in the present tense in the ECC should be read in conjunction with clause 10.1 (Actions), which contains the obligatory 'shall' and which reaches out to all actions made in accordance with the contract and turns all actions into commands.

The ECC is in effect meant to be an everyday working document: it provides the procedures that create the rights and obligations. Drafting the ECC in the present tense makes it more like ordinary everyday language and is an indication that it is a working document. All NEC documents minimise the use of legalese and this assists in the understanding of the contract and the actions required under it.

> The ECC is an everyday working document.

1.5.2 Clause numbering

The first clause number is clause 10. Some users might find this a little strange, particularly if, again, comparisons are made to traditional contracts where the first clause might be clause 1.

The clause numbering assists users in navigating their way through the core clauses. There are nine sections of core clauses. Each clause within the first section of core clauses (1 General) starts with a number 1. Each clause within the second section of core clauses (2 The *Contractor*'s main responsibilities) starts with a number 2. And so on. If clause 52.1 is referred to, then you know that it can be found in the fifth section of core clauses (5 Payment). The second digit in the clause number refers to the order in which the clause appears in the section of core clauses. The digit 2 in clause 52.1 is therefore the **third** clause in the section – the first being nought (50.1). The digit after the decimal point refers to the paragraph in the clause. The digit 1 in 52.1 therefore means that it is the **first** paragraph in clause 52.

1.5.3 Defined terms

Defined terms are words and phrases that begin with an initial capital letter (in accordance with clause 11.2), such as

- the Site
- the Working Areas
- the Completion Date
- Plant and Materials.

The definition of these defined terms used throughout the ECC can be found in clause 11.2.

1.5.4 Identified terms
1.5.4.1 Generally

Identified terms are words and phrases that appear in italics (in accordance with clause 11.1), such as

- *Project Manager*
- *defect correction period*
- *completion date*
- *law of the contract*.

The data that replace these italicised terms for each individual contract are to be found in the Contract Data.

> If, for example, Harry Haste has been named as the *Project Manager* in the Contract Data of a particular contract, then every time the *Project Manager* is referred to in the *conditions of contract*, it is Mr Harry Haste who is required to fulfil the actions described.

Note that some identified terms (in italics) also have capital initials, such as *Employer* or *Project Manager*. The capital initials do not make an italicised phrase a defined term. The italics take precedence and the term is an identified term to be found in the Contract Data.

1.5.4.2 Completion Date/*completion date*

You might notice that *completion date* is an identified term as well as a defined term (Completion Date). This means that the *completion date* can be found in the Contract Data and that the definition of the Completion Date is to be found in clause 11.2.

> Let us suppose that the *completion date* stated in the Contract Data is 19th of July 2012. The definition of the Completion Date (clause 11.2(3)) is 'The Completion Date is the *completion date* unless later changed in accordance with this contract.' The definition therefore refers you to the Contract Data and the 19th of July 2012 stated therein. Wherever the *conditions of contract* refer to the Completion Date, you know that it means the 19th of July 2012.

> For example, clause 30.1 states that 'The *Contractor* . . . does the work so that Completion is on or before the Completion Date.' In this contract, therefore, the *Contractor* is required to complete the *works* by 19th of July 2012. Of course, this date may change during the period of the contract if, for example, a compensation event results in a later Completion Date. If this happens, then the Completion Date refers to the new date as changed in accordance with the contract.

1.5.4.3 Working Areas/*working areas*

A similar definition exists for the Working Areas, where the definition of the Working Areas is as follows.

> Clause 11.2(18): 'The Working Areas are those parts of the *working areas* which are
> - necessary for Providing the Works and
> - used only for work in this contract
> unless later changed in accordance with this contract.'

The *working areas* are identified in Contract Data part two by the *Contractor*. The *working areas* can be changed by agreement between the *Contractor* and the *Project Manager* (clause 15.1). Any reference to the Working Areas therefore refers the user to the areas identified in Contract Data part two and any other areas that may have been added later.

1.5.4.4 Plant and Materials *and* Equipment

Depending on your traditional background or discipline, you may have a different idea of the definition of Plant and Materials (clause 11.2(12)) and Equipment (clause 11.2(7)) than intended in the ECC. Plant and Materials are items that are intended to be included in the *works*. Plant in this definition refers to items of mechanical and electrical engineering services installations. It should be noted that some disciplines would refer to these installations as items of equipment (note the use of the lower case 'e'). This should not be confused with the use of the word Equipment in the ECC.

Equipment (note comments on Plant and Materials in the paragraph above) are items provided by the *Contractor* and used by him to Provide the Works and which the Works Information does not require him to include in the *works*. This definition covers items traditionally known as constructional plant (note the use of the lower case 'p'), for example, excavators, cranes, temporary works such as temporary sheet piling.

1.5.4.5 Difference between identified and defined terms

To emphasise the difference between identified terms and defined terms, we can look at clause 50.1. Table 1.2 shows identified terms and defined terms that can be found in this clause.

1.5.5 Contract data numbering

You may notice when you look at the pro-forma for the Contract Data as it appears in the black book (the Engineering and Construction Contract has a black cover in its published form and is known as the 'black book' to distinguish it from the contracts A to F in the boxed set), that all sections of core clauses are listed down the left-hand side of the page, except for core clause sections 2, 7 and 9. This is because there are no **new** identified terms appearing in these sections of the core clauses.

To explain further, the identified term tends to appear in the Contract Data under the core clause section in which it first appears, in the conditions of contract. For example, the identified terms *Project Manager* (clause 10.1), *Employer* (clause 10.1), *Supervisor* (clause 10.1), *boundaries of the site* (clause 11.2(15)), and *language of the contract*

Table 1.2. Examples of defined and identified terms

Defined terms	Identified terms
Parties Completion Defects Certificate	*Project Manager* *assessment interval* *starting date* *works* *Supervisor*
These are defined terms because they have capital initial letters	These are identified terms because they are in italics
These terms are defined in clause 11.2	These terms are identified in the Contract Data

(clause 13.1), among others, all appear in section 1 of the core clauses and are subsequently named in section 1 General of Contract Data part one.

Going back to clause 50.1 as discussed above, the identified terms in that clause appear in different places in Contract Data part one according to where they first appeared in the *conditions of contract*.

- *Project Manager* therefore appears in section 1 of Contract Data part one because the term *Project Manager* first appears in clause 10.1.
- The term *assessment interval* appears in section 5 of Contract Data part one because it has not been referred to in previous sections of core clauses.
- The term *starting date* appears in section 3 of Contract Data part one because this term first appears in clause 31.2.
- The term *works* appears in section 1 of Contract Data part one because this term first appears in clause 11.2(13).
- *Supervisor* appears in section 1 of Contract Data part one because the term *Supervisor* first appears in clause 10.1.

In general, therefore, if the identified term refers to

1 a general item, it will appear in section 1 of Contract Data part one
2 time, it will appear in section 3 of Contract Data part one
3 testing and Defects, it will appear in section 4 of Contract Data part one
4 payment, it will appear in section 5 of Contract Data part one
5 compensation events, it will appear in section 6 of Contract Data part one
6 risks and insurance, it will appear in section 8 of Contract Data part one.

The two exceptions to this generalisation are

- the identified terms that appear in Contract Data part two not Contract Data part one
- optional Contract Data statements that should be integrated into the relevant core clause sections in the Contract Data.

1.5.5.1 Exception 1: Contract Data part two

Some identified terms will not be found in Contract Data part one. Examples are

- the *Contractor*
- the *working areas*
- the *activity schedule*
- the *bill of quantities*.

Although the *Contractor* is first mentioned in clause 10.1 and you might therefore expect to find it identified in section 1 of Contract Data part one, it is, in fact, to be found in Contract Data part two. The terms mentioned in the list above are terms that the *Contractor* has to provide as part of his tender and therefore they are included in Contract Data part two. Apart from identifying the *Contractor*, all the other terms pertain to the manner in which the *Contractor* is paid and therefore they are within his scope of influence and not the *Employer*'s.

1.5.5.2 Exception 2: Optional statements

There are a number of 'optional statements' in the pro-forma for the Contract Data included in the ECC. These optional statements represent part of the contract strategy (Contract strategy is discussed in Chapter 1 of Book 2 and examples given in Chapter 3 of Book 2) decided by the *Employer* prior to placing the contract. Although the example of Contract Data in the ECC guidance notes retains these optional statements as a separate section, found after the Contract Data sections for the core clauses, it is recommended that they are in fact integrated into the body of the Contract Data to preserve the logic of the layout. In other words, the optional statement for the *completion date* should be added into section 3 of the Contract Data (assuming the *Employer* chooses the *completion date*). The optional statement regarding additional compensation events should appear under section 6 of the Contract Data. And so on. (An example of the Contract Data with guidance notes is given in Chapter 3 of Book 2.)

> It is recommended that the optional statements are integrated into the body of the Contract Data to preserve the logic of the layout.

1.5.5.3 Conclusion

The foregoing discussion is important because it helps you to locate identified terms in the Contract Data and understand the reasoning behind their placement.

1.5.5.4 The giving of reasons

In general, if a decision is to be made (generally by the *Project Manager*), then the scope of the reasons for that decision are set out in the contract. Examples are clauses 13.4 (reply to a communication is not acceptance) and 31.3 (reasons for not accepting a programme). All of these reasons relate back to clause 60.1(9), where a compensation event may be notified if the *Project Manager* withholds an acceptance for a reason not stated in the contract.

If the reasons given by the *Project Manager* for his decision are not in line with the scope of the reasons stated in the contract, then the *Contractor* becomes entitled to an assessment (this assessment could be for zero time and no extra money; the point is that the *Project Manager*'s withholding acceptance for a reason other than those stated in the contract is a compensation event) of time and money to compensate him for the *Project Manager* breaching his obligations.

Exceptions to this rule requiring specific reasons are clauses 24.2 (removing people) and 36.2 (acceleration) where the *Project Manager* and the *Contractor* respectively are required to give reasons, but any reason may be given.

> Reasons are to be given and the scopes of the reasons for the decisions are set out in the contract.

1.6 Concepts

The following subsections give some of the concepts that are new to the ECC or that are different in the ECC.

1.6.1 Mutual trust and cooperation

The most important aspect of the NEC contracts is the principle of mutual trust and cooperation. The contract is designed so that the *Contractor* is motivated to fulfil his actions and the *Project Manager* and the *Supervisor* are motivated to perform theirs. This principle is so important that, if the *Contractor* does not carry it through to the sub-contracts, the *Project Manager* may refuse to accept the subcontract conditions of contract (clause 26.3).

> Spirit of mutual trust and cooperation is a fundamental principle of the ECC.

1.6.2 Early warning

Change, however big or small, is considered to be almost inevitable in construction contracts and the major source of cost and time uncertainty. An 'early warning' of the change enables the parties to manage the effects of change more effectively.

Traditional contracts do not tend to make it an express obligation to give an early warning of cost-increasing/delaying events. The ECC however includes a specific obligation in clause 16 for the Parties to give notice as soon as they become aware of any matter which could affect the time, cost or quality objectives of the project.

Either the *Project Manager* or the *Contractor* could notify an early warning. Note that the warning is of something in the future (as denoted by the word 'could') and therefore it might not happen at all. This procedure embodies the ECC principle that '*Foresight applied collaboratively mitigates problems and shrinks risk*' (the Engineering and Construction Contract Guidance Notes (ECC2) page 3 paragraph 2).

This early warning procedure (incorporating the risk reduction meeting) provides for

- clear actions by the parties
- joint consideration of proposals to mitigate or avoid the issue
- agreement on joint solutions to the problem
- decisions upon actions to be taken and who will take them
- recording of the proposals considered and decisions taken.

An early warning is contractualised common sense and is an extension of the obligation contained in clause 10.1 to act in the spirit of mutual trust and cooperation. It tends to be far more productive and economical to sort out a problem before it occurs, rather than to wait until after the fact, when your options are reduced and the effects tend to be magnified.

There is no reply *per se* required to an early warning notification.

1.6.2.1 Early warning procedure

Either the notifying party or the recipient of the notification may instruct the other to attend a risk reduction meeting if the matter is considered sufficiently urgent to require immediate attention. Meetings are then held at which a jointly agreed course of action to eliminate or reduce the effects of the notified matter is determined. Otherwise, early warnings may practically be discussed at a regular meeting, such as a weekly progress meeting. This is the only time that the *Contractor* may instruct the *Project Manager* to do something.

The sanction (clause 63.5) for a *Contractor* failing to give an early warning, which could have allowed actions to have been taken to reduce costs and save time, is that if the matter subsequently becomes a compensation event, the *Project Manager* can request that any savings in time and money that would have been made had an early warning been given are taken into account in assessing the effects of the compensation event.

There are no sanctions in the ECC against the *Project Manager* for failing to give an early warning. However, failure to give an early warning could result in greater time, cost or both for the *Employer*'s project. This should be a powerful incentive for the *Employer* to ensure that his appointed *Project Manager* performs. It could also be argued that the *Project Manager* is in breach of clause 10.1 because he has not acted in a spirit of mutual trust and cooperation.

There could be a slight overlap between early warnings and compensation events because compensation events can also be notified for events that will happen (that is, are in the future) but have not yet happened.

In general, then, *Contractors* should be aware of matters that could affect the project and that, if they occur, could reduce the *Project Manager*'s ability to manage the project effectively. It is not in either Party's interests for the *Contractor* to flood the *Project Manager* with early warnings, however, and the spirit of mutual trust and cooperation that underlies the contract should always be borne in mind.

> - **There are sanctions** for the failure of the *Contractor* to give an early warning.
> - Failure by the *Project Manager* to give early warnings may result in the *Employer* incurring greater cost, time or an end-product of reduced quality.

1.6.2.2 Early warning and risk reduction procedure

The early warning procedure centres on the time, cost and quality effects on the project. With regard to the time effects, the subject of an early warning notice could be not only a delay in meeting the Completion Date, but also a delay in meeting a Key Date. A Key Date is set by the *Employer* using the Contract Data and it represents the date by which the *Contractor* is required to meet the *condition*, also stated in the Contract Data. The facility is therefore available to control time more tightly.

With regard to the cost effects, the *Contractor* may notify the *Project Manager* of any matter that could increase his total cost. This all-encompassing category does not appear to limit the *Contractor* to those aspects of the project that are outside of his control. This facility could become burdensome to the *Project Manager*; even though a specific answer is not required from the *Project Manager*, he would still be obliged to review each notice as part of his project management duties.

Clause 16.1 makes it clear that if a compensation event has previously been notified, an early warning for the same subject is not required. This would appear to be common sense since a matter cannot be an *early* warning if it has already been notified as a compensation event.

At the risk reduction meeting (clause 16.2) every early warning automatically becomes a risk to be included in the Risk Register (clause 11.2(14)), the meeting does not discuss early warnings, but rather discusses the registered risk; that is, those risks that were originally in the Risk Register by being listed in the Contract Data, and all the early warning matters. In addition to making proposals for risk avoidance, seeking solutions and deciding on actions, the attendees at the risk reduction meeting decide which risks can be removed from the Risk Register (clause 16.3).

In clause 16.4, the *Project Manager*'s role is more wide-reaching. Rather than simply recording proposals and decisions at the meeting and copying his notes to the *Contractor*, he revises the Risk Register and issues the revised register to the *Contractor*. If any decision has ramifications with regard to a change to the Works Information, the *Project Manager* is proactively required to instruct any change at the same time as he issues the revised register.

1.6.3 Compensation events

The extension of time and financial evaluation provisions in respect of the effects of change in traditional contracts do not lend themselves to giving certainty of outcome to either the *Employer* or *Contractor*. This inevitably leads to dissatisfaction and can cause the breakdown in the communication/collaboration that is so often essential to the success of contracts.

The ECC or the Shorter Schedule of Cost Components uses compensation events to determine change and the Schedule of Cost Components to value change. Compensation events are those events for which the *Contractor* becomes entitled to an assessment of time and money, bearing in mind that the assessment could be zero. Compensation events tend to be a contractual remedy to the *Project Manager*'s or the *Employer*'s breach of contract.

Neither the originally tendered *activity schedule* (main Option A) nor the priced *bill of quantities* (main Option B) is used for assessing the financial effects of change. Instead the *Contractor* is reimbursed the financial effects of the compensation event upon Defined Cost or forecast Defined Cost. The premise behind this is that the *Contractor* should be neither better off, nor any worse off, for the change occurring. (Note that the *Contractor* and the *Project Manager* can agree to use rates and lump sums in accordance with clause B63.13 and D63.13.)

The financial and time effects of compensation events (some of which could constitute variations to the contract) are intended to be pre-assessed within strict time limits and the contractual procedure describes the actions taken by both the *Contractor* and the *Project Manager* to notify, quote for and implement the compensation event.

The most important concept is that the *Contractor* has eight weeks only to notify a matter as a compensation event. The trigger is the *Contractor*'s becoming aware of the event, and this brings with it all the uncertainties of when he became aware of the event. As with the early warning notification, however, documentation and observation will tend to show whether the *Contractor* had knowledge of the matter. If however the matter is one which should have been notified by the *Project Manager*, then there does not appear to be any time limit on notification of the matter as a compensation event.

The reason for these requirements is to ensure that the financial and time effect of all compensation events are assessed at the time they arise and not retrospectively. The time periods included in the contract for the administration of compensation events can be extended by agreement between the *Project Manager* and the *Contractor*. Such extensions should, however, be the exception and not used to cover up ineffective administration of the contract.

1.6.4 Acceleration

Many contracts do not provide any provision for acceleration of the works. Acceleration under ECC means bringing the Completion Date forward. This differs from many contracts where 'acceleration' means speeding up the work to ensure that the Completion Date is achieved. Acceleration is covered in clause 36 and there are also some clauses in the main Options (clause 36.3 in Options A, B, C and D; clause 36.4 in Options E and F) denoting the different ways of implementing acceleration for the different main Options.

The *Project Manager* has no authority to instruct the *Contractor* to accelerate. He may only instruct the *Contractor* to submit a quotation to do so (clause 36.1). The *Contractor* may either submit a quotation or give his reasons for not submitting a quotation (clause 36.2). In other words, the *Contractor* may choose whether to accelerate or not. He is not obliged to accelerate and it may not be imposed upon him. The quotation does not have to be in accordance with Defined Cost plus Fee (as it would generally be for a compensation event quotation), and therefore could be whatever the *Contractor* wishes to charge (always within the boundaries of mutual trust and cooperation, of course). The *Contractor* is required to submit details of his assessment with each quotation (clause 36.1), which seems to suggest that the *Project Manager* may scrutinise and question any details.

If the *Project Manager* is concerned because a compensation event is pushing out the Completion Date, rather than instruct a quotation for acceleration he may request the *Contractor* to submit alternative quotations for dealing with a compensation event, including an alternative quotation maintaining the Completion Date (see Chapter 2 of Book 3 for more details).

Acceleration in the ECC does not mean speeding up the progress of the contract to achieve Completion on time. The *Project Manager* may not instruct the *Contractor* to speed up progress if he is concerned that Completion or that Key Dates are not going to be met. He may, however, instruct the *Contractor* to submit a revised programme (clause 32.2) showing how he intends to make up the lost time. Some *Employers* do not like this departure from traditional contracts where the *Contractor* is required to use his best endeavours and where the *Project Manager* may instruct the *Contractor* to speed up the works in order to meet the contractual completion date. These *Employers* add Option Z clauses allowing the *Project Manager* to make such an instruction and permitting him to disallow the costs of such progression.

Such courses of action and instructions need to be carefully considered by the *Employer*, since such tactics could be seen as coercing/pressuring the *Contractor* to take courses of action which could increase the likely risk of a health and safety incident, for example, methods of working, sequencing of works. Should such an incident occur then the *Contractor* will be culpable but if it was seen by the Health and Safety Executive that the *Employer* had unduly pressurised the *Contractor* into unsuitable actions then the *Employer* may also be held partly culpable for any health and safety incident which may occur.

1.6.5 Adjudication

The only means of dispute resolution in many forms of contract is arbitration or litigation, both of which in recent years have become time-consuming and expensive. The ECC recognises the need to have an intermediate stage of independent dispute resolution and this has been introduced in the form of adjudication.

The contract encourages the resolution of disputes during the currency of the contract and the adjudication process gives clear time-scales and clear actions.

If a Party is dissatisfied with the *Adjudicator*'s decision, then that Party may refer the disputed matter to arbitration or litigation (the choice of arbitration or litigation as the second level of dispute resolution is indicated in Contract Data part one where the *tribunal* is identified). Notification by a Party of his intention to refer a matter to the *tribunal* must be given within four weeks of a disputed *Adjudicator*'s decision.

Adjudication was initiated as a contract dispute method by the NEC and was then introduced as a statutory requirement by the Housing Grants, Construction and Regeneration Act (1996). Because of the definition of a construction contract in the Act, there are still many ECC contracts that do not fall within the definition of a construction contract and therefore do not fall under the remit of the Act, which would generally supersede the ECC adjudication clauses (Option W1). These contracts may still use the ECC adjudication as the first level of dispute resolution, as was intended by the contract. Contracts outside the UK that are not bound by the Housing Grants, Construction and Regeneration Act (1996) may also still use the ECC adjudication as the first level of dispute resolution, as was intended by the contract (through Option W1).

1.6.6 Assessment dates

Assessments of the amount due take place at described assessment dates, generally at monthly intervals. These may have been referred to as interim valuations in traditional contracts. In the ECC, it is the *Project Manager* who assesses the amount due, although he takes into account any application for payment that the *Contractor* might submit. It is not obligatory for the *Contractor* to submit an application for payment although under the cost-based options C, D and E assessment of the amount due could be difficult for the *Project Manager* without an application for payment from the *Contractor*.

1.6.7 Accepted programme

Traditional contracts such as the ICE 5th, 6th and 7th require the *Contractor* to submit a programme for the works within 21 days after the acceptance of his tender. There is no requirement or obligation for a regularly updated programme to be submitted or maintained thereafter.

The ECC recognises that a live up-to-date programme can be a valuable management tool in giving certainty of outcome. It is a contractual requirement for the *Contractor* to maintain an up-to-date programme. This programme provides a contemporary record of progress, identifies the effects of any compensation events (changes) and alerts the *Contractor* to any delays, enabling corrective action to be taken.

If the *Contractor* fails to submit a first programme to the *Project Manager* for acceptance the *Project Manager* withholds a quarter of the Price for Work Done to Date (clause 50.3) from payments until the *Contractor* complies.

The sanction against the *Contractor* who fails to provide a regularly updated programme during the currency of the contract is that the *Project Manager* will be entitled to make his own assessment of any compensation events that arise (clauses 64.1 and 64.2).

Each programme that is submitted to the *Project Manager* for acceptance becomes the Accepted Programme once the *Project Manager* has accepted it. Programmes are submitted regularly and each subsequent programme accepted by the *Project Manager* becomes the Accepted Programme. All assessments are made in accordance with the Accepted Programme and this programme therefore forms a kind of as-built programme as time goes by.

> There is a sanction on the *Contractor* for failure to submit a first programme for acceptance for the *works* within the required period after his tender (see optional statements in Contract Data part one): the *Project Manager* may withhold a quarter of the Price for Work Done to Date.

1.6.8 Design

There is no designer in the ECC. The *Employer*, the *Contractor* or both may carry out the design. If the *Employer* employs an external designer (possibly under a Professional

Services Contract) then the *Employer* is responsible for the design under the ECC contract as if he had done it himself.

If both Parties carry out some parts of the design, the interfaces between the Parties should be very clearly identified in the Works Information.

> The ECC relies on the Works Information to identify the parts of the *works* that the *Employer* and *Contractor* are to design.

1.6.9 Periods for reply All procedures in the ECC give clear time limits in which actions are to be taken and all communications are required to be made within this time limit unless otherwise stated in the contract. There are two places in which these time-scales can be found

1 within the core clauses; for instance, the procedural time-scales and limits for communications relating to compensation events and time are stated within those sections of the Contract (Sections 6 and 3 of the core clauses respectively)
2 the time limit known as the *period for reply* which is stated in Contract Data part one, completed by the *Employer* and which is a default time period applying to all communications that do not have their own time-scale as indicated in item (1) above.

Other time limits, which override the default *period for reply,* can be introduced by way of procedures being inserted into the Works Information. For example, if the *Contractor* is designing the *works* then a detailed *Employer* design approval procedure may be incorporated into the Works Information. (It should be noted, however, that there is generally no 'approval' in the ECC, only acceptance. The *Project Manager* is not required to approve the *Contractor*'s design, but to accept it, since under clause 14.1, the *Contractor* still retains liability for his design.)

Unless another time period is stated, you are tied into the default *period for reply*. The *period for reply* should be tailored to meet the following requirements.

- Internal procedures: for example, the organisation's design approval process might use or require adherence to different time-scales. This can be overcome by including it in the Works Information.
- Type of work: for example, road maintenance schemes or possession work on rail or projects where the facilities are required to be kept in operation will require different consideration in terms of the *period for reply*. There are limited periods of working windows on such projects, for example, nightwork, Sunday working, or a limited time basis (e.g. 11 pm to 5 am). For such projects rapid decisions need to be made to make the most of these working windows. In such circumstances the *period for reply* will need to be very short, for example, one day rather than an advisory 14 days.
- Contractual interfaces: this is particularly important for *Contractors* who complete Contract Data part one in their subcontracts. The Subcontractors' *period for reply* needs to work within the *Contractor*'s own main contractual *period for reply*.
- On the understanding that there may be more than one *period for reply* stated in the contract with a description for the application of each period.

The *period for reply* therefore applies to all people involved in the Contract including the *Project Manager* and *Supervisor*. Failure by the *Project Manager* or *Supervisor* to reply within the required period is a compensation event (clause 60.1(6)).

The sanctions for failure to reply for the *Contractor* are numerous and include the possible loss of entitlement to compensation, or the *Project Manager* making his own assessment of change. These are covered in more detail in the specific chapters which deal with these aspects of the contracts.

It is therefore very important that all parties give consideration to and put in place procedures and set up their organisational structure to deal with communications.

> - The default period is stated in Contract Data part one.
> - The procedures relating to compensation events and the Accepted Programme have their own time-scales.
> - The Works Information may introduce other time limits for procedures dealing with, say, management.
> - The *period for reply* may vary from contract to contract.
> - The *period for reply* should be tailored to meet the requirements of the project, for example, internal procedures, type of work and contractual interfaces.
> - The *period for reply* applies to all parties.

1.6.10 Communications

It is important to note that all communications required by the contract should be communicated separately as required in clause 13.7.

Examples of notifications required by the contract include early warning notices, a notification of a compensation event and a notification of an ambiguity or inconsistency. These notifications are required to be communicated separately, preferably on their own standard form. This means that they cannot be hidden away in minutes of meetings or as part of a letter covering other matters.

The objective is to ensure that important/vital contractual communications are not lost in the everyday hurly burly of contracts. Therefore having a requirement to notify separately ensures that

- the communications type can be clearly identified and
- the communication can be given the appropriate level of action.

In traditional contracts where no such requirement exists then often vital information or notices are lost within a blur of words in letters and reports. Some people and organisations have developed all-singing and all-dancing pro-formas to cover a multitude of communications on one form. This cuts down on the number of different forms required; however, it does require great rigour and discipline to ensure that vital information is not overlooked or not prioritised properly on forms which all look the same.

> - Good communication is vital on all projects.
> - All communications required by the contract should be communicated separately.

1.7 Terminology
1.7.1 Completion

Completion is a defined term that makes reference to the Works Information. The *Employer* should ensure that what is required to achieve Completion is clearly described in the Works Information, although the contract now includes a catch-all definition for situations where Completion is not described in the Works Information. The ECC does not cater for mechanical completion, practical completion or substantial completion, and any inclusion of such terms in the Works Information should be avoided. Any requirement for these types of completion needs to be catered for within the description of Completion in the Works Information. Completion is when the *Contractor* has done everything the Works Information requires him to do by the Completion Date (clause 11.2(2)). This could include as-built drawings, operation manuals, or the requirement for certain tests to have been achieved, or you could ask to receive these things within a specified period after Completion. In the latter case, there is little incentive for the *Contractor* to produce the described items since he would have been paid at Completion prior to submitting the documents.

Completion can only take place when the *Contractor* has corrected notified Defects which would have prevented the *Employer* from using the *works* or Others from doing their work (clause 11.2(2)). This correlates with clause 43.2 where Defects notified before Completion need only be corrected after Completion, except obviously those that prevent the *Employer* from using the *works* – otherwise Completion would not be achieved in the first place.

It is most important to describe Completion in the Works Information in objective terms such that the *Project Manager* can determine whether Completion has been achieved or not (clause 30.2). Difficulties may arise where the *Employer* fails to describe Completion in the Works Information. *Employer*s often omit to describe Completion because they are still thinking in terms of practical or substantial or mechanical completion. Because practical or substantial or mechanical completion are not included in the Works Information, nor described, the problem remains. Although ECC3 has a get-out clause (clause 11.2(2)), it is still recommended to include a description of Completion in the Works Information.

Completion is a status and it is a separate concept from the Completion Date. Completion could take place on, before or after the Completion Date. The *Project Manager* decides the date of Completion (clause 30.2) in accordance with the definition included in the Works Information.

> - The Works Information should include objective statements on what has to be completed for Completion to be achieved.
> - The objective statement for Completion might need to include temporary as well as the permanent *works* solution, for example, temporary staircases to work shafts – they are not part of the final *works* but are intended for use by a follow-on contractor as access.

1.7.2 Take over

Take over takes place within two weeks after Completion (clause 35.1). The principal reason for identifying take over is to mark the point where loss of or damage to the *works* becomes an *Employer*'s risk (clause 80.1). Take over may trigger a compensation event where it happens before both Completion and the Completion Date (clause 60.1(15)) unless the take over falls within the parameters described in clause 35.2 and is included in the Works Information. The *Employer* does not have to take over the *works* before the Completion Date if the optional statement in the Contract Data part one was included (clause 35.1) stating that the *Employer* is unwilling to take over the *works* before the Completion Date.

Take over is also important because it is the primary reason for an *Employer* to choose the secondary Option pertaining to sectional completion (Option X5). If the *Employer* wants to take over parts of the *works* as they are completed, then this secondary Option should be chosen as part of the contract strategy, where the *completion date* for different *sections* of the *works* may be described. Take over for each part would take place within two weeks of each relevant Completion.

It should be noted that there is no allowance within the ECC to have different *defects dates* for different *completion dates*. The *defects date* is a period of time after Completion of the whole of the *works*; therefore if the contract is of long duration with sectional completion and multiple take over, the *defects date* is still triggered by the last Completion – that of the whole of the *works*. *Sections* of the *works* completed earlier would therefore be subjected to a longer period during which the *Contractor* has to correct Defects and so on. The *Employer* in the Contract Data part one can rectify this, however, where he could amend the statement in the Contract Data to give different *defects date*s for different *sections* of the *works*. This could increase the administrative burden and may not work if the functioning of the *works* as a whole is dependent on the adequate functioning of all its parts (if earlier Defects are corrected, however, it should work).

> Take over marks the point were loss or damage to the *works* becomes the *Employer*'s risk.

1.7.3 Schedule of Cost Components and Shorter Schedule of Cost Components

The Schedule of Cost Components (SCC) and Shorter Schedule of Cost Components (SSCC) lists the components of cost for which the *Contractor* is reimbursed Defined Cost. The use of the SCC and/or SSCC is dependent on the main Option selected. The list interacts with the data provided by the *Contractor* for the SCC in Contract Data part two. It is not to be confused with a schedule of rates.

1.7.4 Defects

Defects are defined in the contract as a part of the *works* that is not in accordance with the Works Information (clause 11.2(5)). In other words, if the requirement is not included in the Works Information as something that the *Contractor* is to provide, not providing it cannot be a Defect. Every defect need not be a Defect and instructing the *Contractor* to correct something that is not a Defect (although it could be a defect) is in fact a compensation event.

1.7.5 Contract Date

The Contract Date is the date when the contract comes into existence (clause 11.2(4)). This would generally depend on how offer and acceptance is effected as governed by jurisdiction. The Contract Date would generally be labelled as such in the Articles of agreement/form of contract (see mention of this in Appendix 2 of Book 2) signed by both Parties, since there is no space provided for it in the Contract Data.

The Contract Date should not be confused with *starting date*, which is when time (programme) starts, and when the *Contractor* is on risk.

1.7.6 Defects date

There is no defects liability period or maintenance period *per se* in the ECC. The period within which the *Contractor* is obliged to correct Defects free of charge is the period between Completion of the whole of the *works* and the *defects date*. The *defects date* is stated in the Contract Data part one as being a number of weeks after Completion of the whole of the *works*, usually 52 weeks, sometimes 26 weeks, but it would depend entirely on the *works*. Since the *defects date* is dependent on Completion, it does not matter whether Completion is before, on or after the Completion Date, since the *defects date* runs from Completion and not the Completion Date.

The *defects date* provides three purposes in the ECC.

1   It is the last date by which either the *Supervisor* or the *Contractor* can notify Defects (clause 42.2).
2   It is the date on which the *Supervisor* issues the Defects Certificate (unless a Defect notified before the *defects date* has a *defect correction period* that ends later than the *defects date*, in which case the Defects Certificate is issued on the later date) (clause 43.3).
3   It sets the final date for the notification of compensation events (clause 61.7).

1.7.7 Defect correction period

The *defect correction period* is not to be confused with the *defects date* or the defects liability period or maintenance period in traditional contracts. The *defect correction period* is the maximum period within which a *Contractor* must correct a notified Defect. It is not the whole period from Completion to the *defects date* but a period of, for example, two weeks. Each Defect must be corrected within this period, from its notification or after Completion.

If a Defect is notified before Completion and it does not prevent the *Employer* from using the *works* (if the Defect prevents the *Employer* from using the *works*, then Completion cannot be achieved (clause 11.2(2))), then the Defect must be corrected at Completion (clause 43.2) and it must be corrected within its *defect correction period*, say two weeks. If there are many Defects, the *Contractor* will have to start the correction process before Completion if he is to correct them all within the two weeks.

Defects that are notified after Completion must still be corrected within their *defect correction period*, say two weeks, but the period starts when the Defect is notified (clause 43.2).

There are two further aspects to the *defect correction period* that require some discussion. First, users of maintenance contracts might wish to amend the core clause that requires Defects to be corrected only after Completion. Many contracts require Defects to be corrected at the time of notification; for example, leaving out a danger sign for an overhead line should be immediately corrected. In this case, the second sentence of clause 43.2 would be amended via a secondary Option Z clause to read 'This period begins when the Defect is notified for all Defects.' If the contract is an Option C, D or E contract, Disallowed Cost (clause 11.2(25)) could also be amended via a secondary Option Z clause so that the bullet point reading 'correcting Defects after Completion' is changed to read 'correcting Defects'.

Second, different *defect correction period*s may be introduced for different categories of Defects. The *defect correction period*s for the categories would be stated in the Contract Data part one and the categories described in the Works Information. This may be useful where some Defects require rectification immediately because they would inhibit the functioning of the *works*, while other more cosmetic Defects may be corrected within two or four weeks. Of course, the key is to describe them carefully in the Works Information and to state in Contract Data part one that this is where the descriptions are to be found (see the example in Chapter 5; ECC3 caters for this sort of categorisation in Contract Data part one).

In general, however, careful thought should be invested in the *defect correction period*. Remember also that anything can be changed by agreement and, if the *Contractor* finds that a particular *defect correction period* is too tight regarding a large Defect, the *Project Manager* would be advised to allow the *Contractor* more time to correct the Defect properly.

Various incentive schemes regarding Defects have been used. Although the *Contractor* is supposed to notify his own Defects, traditionally *Contractor*s have not done so and may have been happy to get away with not correcting defects that have not been spotted by the employer and his engineer. In order to encourage the *Contractor* to notify and then correct his own Defects, some *Employer*s change the ECC to disallow the costs of Defects notified by the *Supervisor* but allow the costs of Defects notified by the *Contractor* (this will not work with option A and B contracts). Others split the cost of correcting Defects between the two Parties equally. In Options C, D and E, this may simply encourage the *Contractor* not to notify Defects but correct them anyway, since the cost of such correction would be paid as Defined Cost unless noticed by the *Project Manager* or the *Supervisor* (note, however, that not all Defects are Disallowed Cost).

1.7.8 Access

Access does not mean that the *Contractor* possesses the Site but that he has been given licence to occupy the Site up to the date of Completion, to enter the land and carry out the work.

The *access date* is different from the *starting date*. The *starting date* is the date when the *Contractor* starts the work that he is required to do before he comes on to the Site. The *access date* is when he may start work on Site (clause 30.1). Mobilisation can take place before the *access date* but work on Site may only start on the *access date*. Both the *starting date* and the *access dates* are identified in the Contract Data.

The *Contractor* also identifies on his programme the date by which he requires access, and this date may be later than the *access date* included in the Contract Data (but it may not be earlier) while still achieving Completion on or before the Completion Date. It is a compensation event if

■ the *Employer* does not allow access to and use of each part of the Site by the later of its *access date* and the date shown on the Accepted Programme (clause 60.1(2)).

1.7.8.1 Access on operational facilities

Some projects involve working on facilities which have to be repaired, maintained or renewed while the facility is either kept in operation or during limited periods of time when such works can be undertaken, for example, night-time access, weekend working, annual shutdown for boiler cleans or maintenance on power stations. On such projects access may have to be redefined as the *Contractor* will only have access of the Site/*working areas* at these limited times, say between 11 pm and 5 am. Thereafter the facility will return/be taken over by the *Employer* for his use.

Late return of these types of facilities will also need to be considered and it is usual for there to be delay damages which deal with the late return/take over of the facilities after a period of access by the *Contractor*. These types of damages usually relate to loss of use of facilities, loss of production/income, etc.

These types of requirements can be incorporated by carefully drafted secondary Option Z clauses.

1.7.9 Amending the contract

Great care and consideration should be given prior to amending the ECC. The contract has gone through a great deal of consultation with the construction industry. The contract can therefore be considered to be an industry-agreed standard. Amending the contracts is not something to be encouraged; however, the reality of everyday life means that such an industry-agreed contract cannot deal with all the many and varied situations in which clients find themselves. Examples of these unique circumstances have been referred to in the discussion on possession.

If rewording or redrafting is required it is suggested that it is firstly developed/undertaken by those who understand the *Employer*/the facilities and the particular problems, and then these requirements are translated into the contract by legal advisers who should be required to ensure that they draft such clause(s) in keeping with the ECC contract.

1.8 Terminology not used in the ECC
1.8.1 Extension of time

There is no term 'extension of time' in the ECC. Part of a compensation event quotation is a delay to the Completion Date, which is assessed as the length of time that planned Completion is later than planned Completion shown on the Accepted Programme. Any delay to the Completion Date should not be assessed in isolation from the affect on the Prices.

1.8.2 Variations

Any changes are termed compensation events under the ECC.

1.8.3 Claims

The ECC does not provide for extension of time and variation and loss and expense 'claims' in the way that traditional contracts do. The word 'claim' is not used in the ECC and should not be accepted or considered.

1.8.4 Delay and disruption

There is no such term as 'delay and disruption' under the ECC. The effects of such changes are managed through the compensation event procedure. Time aspects of a delay to the Completion Date, including any disruption to the programme are dealt with through a change to the programme. The financial aspects of a delay to the Completion Date and any disruption to the programme are dealt with through a change to the Prices. The impact of an event is always separated into time and money; there is no separate heading for delay and disruption.

1.8.5 Loss and expense

There is no such concept as 'loss and expense' in the ECC. All events that could entitle the *Contractor* to time and money are listed in section 6 of the core clauses (compensation events) and the procedures for notifying a compensation event and the details of what the *Contractor* may quote for are included in these clauses.

1.8.6 Traditional roles

There is no Engineer/Architect/Purchaser or Employer's Agent in the ECC. The *Project Manager* and the *Supervisor* fill the roles of the *Employer*'s representatives.

There is no mention of either the designer or quantity surveyor in the ECC. These roles, if required, are undertaken via the *Project Manager*.

1.8.7 Subjective measurements

For the most part, subjective measurements have been eradicated from the ECC.

If work were to be performed 'to the satisfaction of the Engineer', the *Contractor* may find this impossible to price for since he does not know what this measurement is, and he might find it frustrating if the Engineer is a difficult person. Other consequences could result, such as an increase in the risk portion in the price.

If, 'in the opinion of the Engineer' something is not right, this again is not measurable and not something for which the *Contractor* can price.

What is reasonable to one person may not be reasonable to another. Certainly, taking 'reasonable' steps or using 'reasonable' endeavours is not measurable and disputes may result because of a difference in opinion. Subjective measures are not fair and it is not right to expect a *Contractor* to take the risk for human dynamics. None of these terms is used in the ECC (although 'reasonably' is used in clauses 61.6 and 63.7).

1.8.8 Preliminaries

Preliminaries do not require a separate mention in the ECC. All items that would tradition-ally have been included under the heading of 'preliminaries' are now included either in the Prices (for Options A and B) or in the Charges or Equipment section of the Schedule of Cost Components or Shorter Schedule of Cost Components (clause 44 and 2 Equipment in FSCC; clause 41 or 2 Equipment of the SSCC).

1.8.9 Provisional sums

The ECC does not refer to and does not cater for the use of provisional sums. The reason for this is that the ethos of the ECC is all about greater certainty of outcome in terms of cost, time and quality.

Provisional sums are recognised as having been used to include ill-defined or unscoped works in contracts. Indeed the JCT form of contract tries to address this with defined and undefined provisional sums, the distinction being that a defined provisional sum has sufficient detail to enable the *Contractor* to allow for the time implications of the work involved. Undefined provisional sums cover work which cannot be adequately defined and are therefore included as *employer* allowances in the contract sum. In the JCT form of contract there are specific clauses which relate to the expenditure of provisional sums.

Where an *Employer* includes a provisional sum in an ECC contract, a number of issues are raised, especially in Option A.

- How are these provisional works assessed/valued?
- Are they to be included in the *activity schedule* and Accepted Programme?
- Can this money only be expended on the instruction of the *Project Manager*?
- What right has the *Project Manager* to issue an instruction relating to provisional sums (bearing in mind it is a fixed-price lump sum)?
- What happens if the provisional sum is wrong? Who owns the under-spend? Who owns the over-spend?
- How do you judge when a compensation event has occurred if there is little or no scope or Works Information?
- How will any saving on provisional sums be repaid to the *Employer*, if there are no instructions or compensation events?

All of these issues need to be discussed and agreed with the *Employer*.

There are two ways in which work of a provisional nature can be included in an ECC contract.

1 A description of the work is included in the Works Information. This description should include the scope and any other factors such as the specification, timing and restraints of the work that affect and enable the *Contractor* to price the work, including a list of assumptions made by the *Employer*. The description could almost be considered as a mini work package. This description will then be used as the basis of the test to determine if a compensation event has happened or is likely to happen

along with the rest of the Works Information. Clearly, if the *Employer*'s assumptions prove to be incorrect, any changes to the Works Information to rectify those assumptions are a compensation event.

2   If the *Employer* is unable adequately to define this work then he should have an internal budget/allowance if he believes that the work is likely to occur. If or when it does arise the *Project Manager* will then issue an instruction, which will be a change to the Works Information, and it will be a compensation event.

1.8.9.1 Example

The following is an example of how a company managed the problem of provisional sums. Although the above two methods are the recommended route, the following exhibits the flexibility that can make the contract work. This example was characterised by the *Employer*'s/*Project Manager*'s desire to include provisional sums being driven by the following.

■   A need to include the potential full value of the works in the contract – an internal budgetary control problem. They did not seem to operate an internal contingency system and did not want to be seen to be going back for more money even though it should have been part of the budget for the project.
■   An inability to be able to clarify the scope/details of the project.

The *Project Manager* was also driven by the desire to be seen to perform well on his Key Performance Indicators (KPIs). These included the number of instructions and compensation events issued. Consequently he was reluctant to issue an instruction with regard to the provisional sums or compensation events because it would affect his KPIs.

It was agreed that

■   the provisional sums were for expenditure by direction of the *Project Manager*; however, he would not issue an instruction or compensation event until the provisional sum was expended
■   assessment of expenditure against the provisional sum would be by using the Schedule of Cost Components
■   any under-expenditure would be subject to an instruction/compensation event
■   the work would be included in the *activity schedule* and on the Accepted Programme so that the time consequences of any change in the scope of the provisional sum or other critical path activities on the provisional sum could be assessed
■   the work would be better defined with assumptions to enable easier determination of compensation events.

The foregoing comments are based on the assumption that there are no Option Z clauses (additional *conditions of contract*) included in the contract that facilitates the use of provisional sums.

1.8.10 Prime Cost Sums

In traditional contracts, Prime Cost Sums are included in contracts for expenditure against works undertaken by nominated subcontractors or suppliers. The ECC does not permit nomination in this way because of the contractual complication it introduces if things go wrong, and therefore Prime Cost Sums are not required.

1.8.11 Interim valuations

Interim valuations under the ECC are called the amount due and include the Price for Work Done to Date. It is a duty of the *Project Manager* to assess the amount due. There is no duty for the *Contractor* to submit an application.

1.8.12 Other contractual aspects

There are other contractual aspects that users may be used to seeing in traditional forms of contract that do not appear as a matter of course in the ECC. Some of these are listed in Table 1.3 together with the place in which they should be inserted.

Table 1.3. Other contractual aspects

Contractual aspect required	How to include it in the ECC
To maintain confidentiality	Insert as an Option Z clause
To proceed regularly and diligently	Insert in Works Information
To inspect the Site	Insert in Works Information
To set out the *works*	Insert in Works Information
To perform variations	This is already included in the ECC by virtue of clause 27.3
To submit interim applications	Not a duty of *Contractor* but of *Project Manager* (clause 50.4)
To notify on completion	Not a duty of *Contractor* but of *Project Manager*
To conform to statutes	This is not strictly required since it is the duty of everybody to adhere to the law. This obligation could be reiterated in the Works Information if deemed absolutely necessary

1.9 Commentary on other aspects of the ECC
1.9.1 Clarity

In general, clarity is an important part of the ECC. Clear clauses are important to the working of the contract.

1.9.2 Contractual forms

Neither the ECC conditions of contract nor the Guidance Notes provide standard forms for

- form of tender (although a sample is provided in the ECC Guidance Notes)
- Articles of agreement/form of contract (although a sample is provided in the ECC Guidance Notes)
- form of performance bond
- form of guarantee.

There is also no stated order of precedence for documents and no place to state the Contract Date (see Appendix 2 of Book 2 where the Contract Date can be inserted into the form of contract/Articles of agreement) in the ECC.

> - There is no hierarchy of documents in NEC contracts.
> - The one exception to this rule is that the *Employer*'s Works Information takes precedence over the *Contractor*'s proposals. The acceptance does not change the *Contractor*'s liability to Provide the Works in accordance with the Works Information.

1.10 How does the ECC affect the way you work?
1.10.1 Mutual trust and cooperation clause 10.1

It is this clause that distinguishes the NEC3 ECC from traditional contracts and you need to bear it in mind all the time.

1.10.2 Fair and reasonable

Part of being trusting and cooperative is being fair and reasonable. Is it fair to deprive the *Contractor* of his profit for a matter that he cannot control? Is it reasonable to expect the *Contractor* to foresee what you expect of him if it is not included in the Works Information? Is it fair to deprive the *Employer* of the opportunity to consider options through early warnings?

1.10.3 Work within your given role

If you are the *Project Manager* or the *Supervisor* or you have been delegated a part of these roles, then you may only do what you are allowed to do under the contract. The *Supervisor* may not change the Works Information and he may not accept a Defect. The *Project Manager* may not notify a Defect and he may not instruct a search for a Defect.

1.10.4 Use the procedures in the contract

The procedures in the contract are well described and well set out. They tell you how to fill your role in the contract. Following the procedures in the contract will introduce trust and fairness into your dealings with each other and will help to fulfil your own, your company's and your client's (where your company is not the *Employer* but is employed to assist the *Employer*) objectives.

1.10.5 Existing knowledge of the law of contract

> The ECC, although radical in its approach, does not require you to forget your existing knowledge and experience of the law of contract.

1.10.6 Proactive project management

The contract is designed to facilitate proactive and collaborative project management, through the use of procedures such as the early warning mechanism and the compensation event procedure. If the project management team adopts this approach, then the contract has the chance of being a success.

1.10.7 Work with each other

Both parties to a contract are there to help each other and to fill the mutual objective of completing the project on time and to budget. If you work with each other, you increase your chances of success.

> **YOU make the project a success**
> No matter how good or bad the contract, it is the people working the contract who make it a success or not. Whether the project is a success is up to you.

1.11 Summarising the ECC

The ECC provides an opportunity to enhance contractual arrangements.

Many commentators have called the ECC a partnering contract. In the authors' view, the ECC can be as partnering or non-partnering as you want it to be. It depends on the attitude of the parties. The contract has features which lend themselves to the partnering model (see Chapter 1 of Book 2 for a discussion on partnering).

The ECC is radically different from other, traditional, forms of contract. It is essential that you realise from the outset what it is you wish to achieve and also to recognise that, in order to achieve the objectives set, you will be required to train yourself, your staff, your contractors, subcontractors and suppliers in its use. As you progress through this series, you will see the strong inter-reliance on information between everyone in the supply chain.

It is also important to realise that the implementation of the use of the ECC could have implications for your own internal procedures, systems and business.

Because of the ECC structure, commonality of approach and flexibility the comments made throughout this book apply equally to employers, contractors, subcontractors and sub-subcontractors.

1.12 Potential benefits

The ECC offers potential benefits to its users through

- managing contracts more efficiently and effectively
- providing greater certainty of outcome
- facilitating final account agreement very shortly after Completion
- compensation events providing a time and money package for change
- an updated programme facilitating time and cost management
- encouraging proactive management
- encouraging parties to work together.

Figure 1.3 Key aspects of the ECC

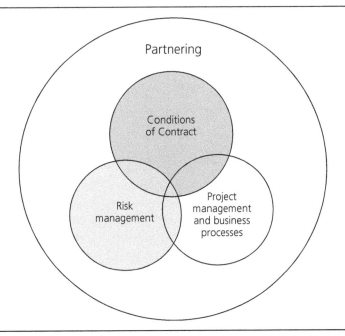

Figure 1.3 shows the key features of the ECC Contract. The ECC incorporates conditions of contract, risk management and a project management and business process management tool. It is also surrounded by the possibility and opportunity to use the contract in the context of a collaborative working environment and partnering.

The ECC brings together three core elements of change control, namely planning, commercial and design management (see Figure 1.4).

> The ECC is all about improving management practice, reducing the number of disputes and improving contract administration to achieve:
>
> **Greater certainty of outcome**

Figure 1.4 The key requirements of change control

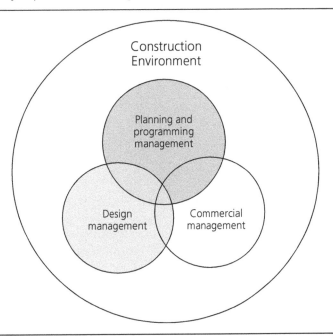

Introduction to the Engineering and Construction Contract
ISBN 978-0-7277-5718-0

ICE Publishing: All rights reserved
doi: 10.1680/iecc.57180.033

Chapter 2
Roles in the Engineering and Construction Contract

Synopsis

This chapter describes the roles adopted in the ECC, including

- how to designate a role
- discussion of the roles described in the ECC
- discussion of the project team
- how the ECC affects each of the roles.

2.1 Introduction

There is no doubt that of the three objectives used in the drafting of the ECC (i.e. stimulus to good management, clarity and simplicity, flexibility), it is stimulus to good management that is the most important. It is certainly the primary reason why so many employers choose to use the ECC. The ECC has been drafted with the conscious objective of promoting good management practice generally, and collaboration between the parties to their mutual benefit and to the benefit of the project overall.

Two of the procedures in the contract that facilitate the stimulus of good management are

- a clear division of function and responsibility in order to identify accountability and motivate people to play their part
- specific time limits within which the various parties are to take the actions described for them with 'sanctions' for failure to do so.

In general, when the ECC states that an action is required, the person who is to carry out the action is stipulated and a time frame for the carrying out of the action is included. Each Party to the contract therefore knows who of the other Party should be taking what actions.

> If you add additional actions/duties in the Works Information, remember to state who carries out that duty and stipulate the time frame if it is different from the default *period for reply*.

2.2 Roles in the ECC

The ECC identifies and describes various roles for the people who are involved in the contract. Some of the people carrying out a role might be part of a project team or in some cases might undertake more than one of the roles. The following list includes the roles identified in the ECC.

- *Project Manager*
- *Supervisor*
- *Employer*
- *Contractor*
- Subcontractor
- Others
- delegates
- *Adjudicator*
- *tribunal*.

> There is no defined role of designer or quantity surveyor in the ECC. These functions are fulfilled where required through the *Project Manager*.

2.3 How to designate a role

The role you have been assigned under the contract does not reflect on your job title or your standing in the organisation. Being named as the *Project Manager* under the contract does not mean that you have to be a Project Manager in the company for which you work. Similarly, if your job title is Project Manager in the company for which you work, that does not mean that you should automatically be named as the *Project Manager* in an ECC contract.

The *Project Manager* and the *Supervisor* and the other roles in the ECC are not specific people in an organisation but roles. They can be thought of as roles that have various duties under the contract. In particular, the choice of *Project Manager* under the contract should be very carefully considered and it is recommended that the person chosen has the authority to be responsible for all the actions required by the *Project Manager* (in particular, the *Project Manager* should be delegated sufficient authority to make decisions about the contract value).

Those identified in the contract under the various roles should be the names of people, not the names of organisations. They should also be the people who actually do the job, not the head of the section or the director of the organisation. This is particularly applicable when consulting engineering organisations are hired by employers to be the *Project Manager* and perhaps also the *Supervisor* in the contract. For example, the *Project Manager* should be Harry Haste, Organisation ABC Inc, Address, and not simply Organisation ABC Inc, Address.

The duties carried out by the *Contractor*, the *Project Manager*, the *Supervisor* and the *Employer* in the ECC are included in Appendix 1 to this chapter.

> The *Project Manager* should be the best person for the job, not necessarily the person whose job title is Project Manager.

2.4 Separation of roles and responsibilities

In traditional contracts such as JCT, ICE, FIDIC, IChemE, the Architect, the Engineer or the Supervising Officer is given total responsibility.

Under ICE contracts for instance, the Engineer is employed by the Client to plan and design the project, to draw up the contract, to obtain tenders, to let and supervise the work, to authorise payment and to issue certificates and to decide upon disputes. An architect under JCT contracts has a similar role. The Architect has a general periodic supervision of the work, but everyday site supervision falls on the Employer and on the Contractor who are required to keep on the works a 'competent person in charge'. The Employer may appoint a clerk of works whose duty is solely to act as inspector on behalf of the Employer but under the direction of the Architect.

In building contracts the design and commercial functions are shared between the Architect and the quantity surveyor whereas the civil engineer retains total responsibility for civil engineering contracts. These contracts put the Engineer, Architect and Supervising Officer on a pedestal with total responsibility and they expect these individuals to be all-knowing beings, who can supervise the works, manage its administration, and carry out all the other functions that the contract requires. They also have a quasi-judicial role to play in the first-stage settlement of any disputes that arise and this can lead to a conflict of interest where the dispute may reflect badly on their own performance.

The ECC recognised that the traditional composite role of the Engineer or Architect was undesirable, and it broke down these functions into four parts with the introduction of a new role of *Employer*'s *Project Manager*. It also recognised the need to have an independent arbiter in the event of disputes.

The four parts, to be occupied by four different people or firms are

1   *Project Manager*
2   *Supervisor*
3   designer
4   *Adjudicator*.

These four parts are now described in more detail below.

2.4.1 The *Project Manager*

The role *Project Manager* carries with it certain actions and duties that have to be fulfilled as *Project Manager*. Those actions may, of course, be delegated, but in essence the *Project Manager* runs the contract and therefore, if actions are delegated to various people, the *Project Manager* should be kept informed in order that the required decisions can be made.

The *Project Manager* is not equivalent to the Engineer in traditional contracts, and the *Supervisor* is not equivalent to the Clerk of Works in traditional contracts. There should be no comparisons and no similar actions taken. All actions are described in the ECC and the *Contractor* has the right to refuse to respond to an instruction given by a person who does not possess the authority either by being named in the contract or through delegation. It is not essential for the *Project Manager* to possess the technical skills of an architect or engineer.

The *Project Manager* is squarely the *Employer*'s man. The contract does not state an obligation for him to act impartially and there is no adjudication role played by the *Project Manager*. The *Project Manager*'s role is moderated by the requirement in Clause 10.1 for the *Project Manager* '...to act as stated in the contract and in a spirit of mutual trust and cooperation, and by the inclusion of the adjudication provisions'.

The *Project Manager* carries out the role of 'contract administrator' on behalf of the *Employer*. The *Project Manager* is the *Employer*'s agent and is responsible for looking after the *Employer*'s interests (but must act in a fair and unbiased manner). The *Project Manager* should be on site regularly, aware of progress and the other aspects of the contract such as changes to the Prices, Defects (note that the *Project Manager* does not notify Defects, but he should still be aware of them) and compensation events that allow him to take reasonable decisions under the contract. The *Project Manager* may delegate some of these actions to other people.

Employers should consider the number of duties and the responsibilities held by a *Project Manager* before naming the same person as *Project Manager* in many contracts. The role of *Project Manager* means that the *Project Manager* is involved in and has responsibility for virtually every aspect of the contract, except perhaps termination, the making of a payment and the duties that are the *Supervisor*'s. As such, to be allocated as *Project Manager* on too many projects could mean a dilution of the time spent on each of them and a consequent reduction of performance.

The *Employer* should also ensure that the *Project Manager* has been given the authority to carry out his duties, for example, to commit the organisation financially on payment certificates, to increase the total of the Prices and to deduct delay damages.

2.4.2 The *Supervisor*

The *Supervisor* is required to ensure that the *works* are provided to the standard and performance required in the Works Information. The *Supervisor* witnesses or carries out tests and inspections, and notifies Defects but may not accept a Defect. The *Supervisor* may not give site instructions or otherwise change the Works Information. If some *Supervisor* actions are delegated to the *Project Manager* (it is recognised that for some smaller jobs this would be the most efficient designation), the latter needs to be very aware of the role that is being undertaken when carrying out certain actions. In other words, the *Project Manager* should be aware which of the duties are to be undertaken in the role of *Supervisor* and which are to be carried out as a delegate of the *Project Manager*.

For example, in an arbitration in 2001/2002, the roles in the contract were confused and the contract ended in dispute. The arbitration was based on a dispute over a number of compensation events and part of the *Contractor*'s defence for carrying out various works was to present as evidence letters written by the *Supervisor* instructing the *Contractor* to correct Defects in a certain manner. In fact, the specific descriptions of the corrections comprised changes to the Works Information, but the *Supervisor* had no such authority to instruct the changes. The *Supervisor* could only notify the Defect. The *Contractor* was therefore not obliged to make the changes, only to correct the Defect so that it complied with the Works Information.

2.4.2.1 The relationship between the *Project Manager* and the *Supervisor*

The *Project Manager* and the *Supervisor* are independent of each other. They do not report one to the other, although communications are copied to each other; for example, the *Supervisor* copies Defect notifications to the *Project Manager*. In other words, there is no line reporting from the *Supervisor* to the *Project Manager* and the *Supervisor* carries out these duties independently of the *Project Manager*. Even if there is line reporting between the person named as the *Project Manager* and the person named as the *Supervisor* as part of their job outwith the contract, this relationship cannot be mirrored in the duties they carry out under the contract.

2.4.3 The designer

Separate functions for the *Employer*'s and *Contractor*'s designer are assumed but not mentioned in the contract. The actions required of the *Employer*'s designer, such as providing revised Works Information when changes occur and accepting the *Contractor*'s designs, are discharged by the *Project Manager*. Since the design provides a large potential for compensation events, this process needs to be carefully managed by the *Project Manager*.

2.4.4 The *Adjudicator*

The *Adjudicator* is the person who provides the first level of dispute resolution under the contract. Assuming that the Parties cannot come to an agreement – a first attempt to resolve the dispute should always be made by the *Project Manager* and the *Contractor* – the dispute is referred to the *Adjudicator*. If the contract falls within the definition of a construction contract in the Housing Grants, Construction and Regeneration Act 1996, then the adjudication procedure should follow that detailed in Option W2, assuming this was chosen by the *Employer*. If the contract falls within the definition of a construction contract in the Housing Grants, Construction and Regeneration Act 1996 but Option W2 was not chosen by the *Employer*, then the default Scheme for Construction will apply. The *Employer* has to make an active choice of Option W1.

The introduction of an *Adjudicator* relieves the *Project Manager* from having to decide upon disputes in which there may be a conflict of interest.

2.4.5 Summary

The different roles and responsibilities between the ECC and traditional contracts can be seen in Table 2.1.

Table 2.1. Comparison of roles and responsibilities between ECC and traditional contracts

Traditional contracts	Engineering and Construction Contract
Composite role	Clear division of functions and responsibility
■ Engineer	■ *Project Manager*
	■ *Supervisor*
■ Architect	■ designer
	■ *Adjudicator*

The ECC therefore provides clear division of function and responsibility and seeks to motivate people to play their part by making it in their professional and commercial interests to do so.

2.5 Other roles in the ECC

2.5.1 The *Employer*

The *Employer* is a Party to the contract but plays very little part in the contract. The *Employer* appoints agents in the form of the *Project Manager* and the *Supervisor* to carry out the actions required under the contract. The *Employer* may become involved for elements of the contract such as termination and, of course, the *Employer* pays the *Contractor*.

2.5.2 The *Contractor*

The *Contractor* is the other Party to the contract and is responsible for all the duties attributed to the *Contractor* under the contract, many of which are detailed in section 2 of the core clauses (the *Contractor*'s main responsibilities).

2.5.3 Subcontractors

Subcontractors are defined in the contract and include all those bodies who contribute to the *Contractor*'s Providing the Works. The ECC does not cater for nominated Subcontractors for practical and legal reasons, for example, renomination if a subcontractor/supplier goes into liquidation.

Alternatives to nomination under the ECC is for

■ a list of acceptable subcontractors/suppliers to be named in the Works Information and the *Contractor* chooses with whom to subcontract, or
■ the *Employer* to employ them under a separate contract.

Figure 2.1 Diagrammatic representation of the relationship of the contract roles

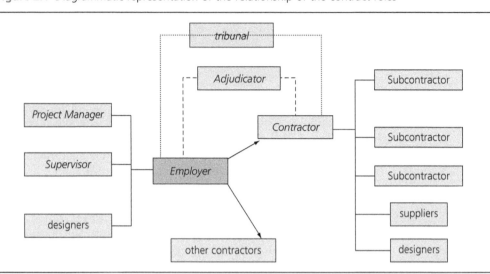

2.5.4 Others

Others are defined in the contract as other people or organisations who do not directly have a role under the contract and would most likely include other contractors, public authorities and utility service providers (gas, electricity, telephone, etc.).

The Works Information should state who are the Others. Where stipulated in the Works Information the *Contractor* will be required to obtain approval for this design from Others (clause 27.1). The *Contractor* should also cooperate with Others (clause 25.1).

> An example of this may be where a new escalator box is to be constructed below an existing communications duct which has very sensitive fibre-optic cables which serve an essential service and are owned by a third-party utility. In this instance, the Works Information should make it very clear about the ownership of the ducts and stipulate that it is the *Contractor*'s responsibility to liaise with and obtain approval for the temporary and permanent design solutions from Others.

In general, the *Employer* takes the responsibility for Others (1) who do not work within the times shown on the Accepted Programme, or (2) who do not work within the conditions stated in the Works Information, or (3) who carry out work on the Site that is not stated in the Works Information (clause 60.1(5)).

2.5.5 The *tribunal*

The *tribunal* is the second level of dispute resolution where adjudication has not achieved the desired results. The *tribunal* is identified in Contract Data part one and could be litigation or arbitration.

Figure 2.1 shows the relationship between the Parties to the contract and the various roles within the contract.

2.6 The project team

Having looked at the philosophy behind the various roles and the contract's organisational requirements, this section goes on to provide the main points for consideration while establishing a project team.

The composition of the project team will depend on

- the *Employer*'s attitude towards having consultants and contractors as part of the project team
- the bigger picture in terms of what other contracts are ongoing on the same site or by the same contractors and consultants, and
- the particular procurement route of the contract, for example, if the designer is a part of the contract team where the contract is *Employer*-designed or if the contract is a design-and-build contract.

2.6.1 Preparation of a project team

The ECC is a management tool that is designed to be used throughout the duration of the contract by all the team members. Its effectiveness depends on how well it is used by the team. In order to increase its effectiveness, it is important to ensure that the following issues are considered.

2.6.1.1 Choice and selection of personnel

The recognition of the benefits of management by collaboration means acknowledging that personalities count and so the choice and selection of personnel on the project is very important. This is one reason why the names of the *Project Manager* and the *Supervisor* are revealed when issuing the invitation to tender letter and accompanying tender documentation, and why the key people put forward by the tenderer are expected to be the same people who work on the project.

The team has to be prepared to cooperate and communicate with each other to make the project work. There is no doubt that a culture change needs to take place for the ECC to work. The people working on the contract are vital to promoting the culture of the ECC. Words on a paper carry little weight unless the people carrying out the contract follow through with the ethos of the ECC.

2.6.1.2 Training

The *Employer* should encourage all team members (including *Contractors* and Subcontractors) to become familiar with the *conditions of contract* and the underlying concepts of the contract. This could involve joint training for all the project team, including the *Contractor* and his Subcontractors, so that the whole team knows the results of their actions and the impact on the whole team.

It is recommended that teams be brought together for workshops centred on the project so that real-life situations are described and recognised by the team.

2.6.1.3 Project organisation

The project organisation should contain chart and job descriptions and should include clear lines of communication so that everybody knows what everyone else is doing.

2.6.1.4 Management systems

The appropriate management systems for the project should be agreed by the team, put in place and implemented. Training should also be provided, if required. Figure 2.2 shows how an Employer's team would be traditionally organised.

It could be suggested that for ECC contracts, the structure should be different. Figure 2.3 shows the key players as referred to in the contract and it shows the key functions which either the *Project Manager* will have to undertake or which will be undertaken by other firms of consultants or individuals appointed by the *Employer* or by the *Employer*'s own in-house teams.

Figure 2.2 Traditional *Employer*'s team

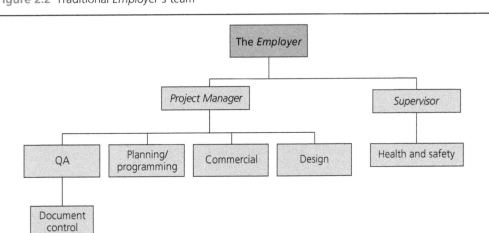

Figure 2.3 The *Employer*'s team

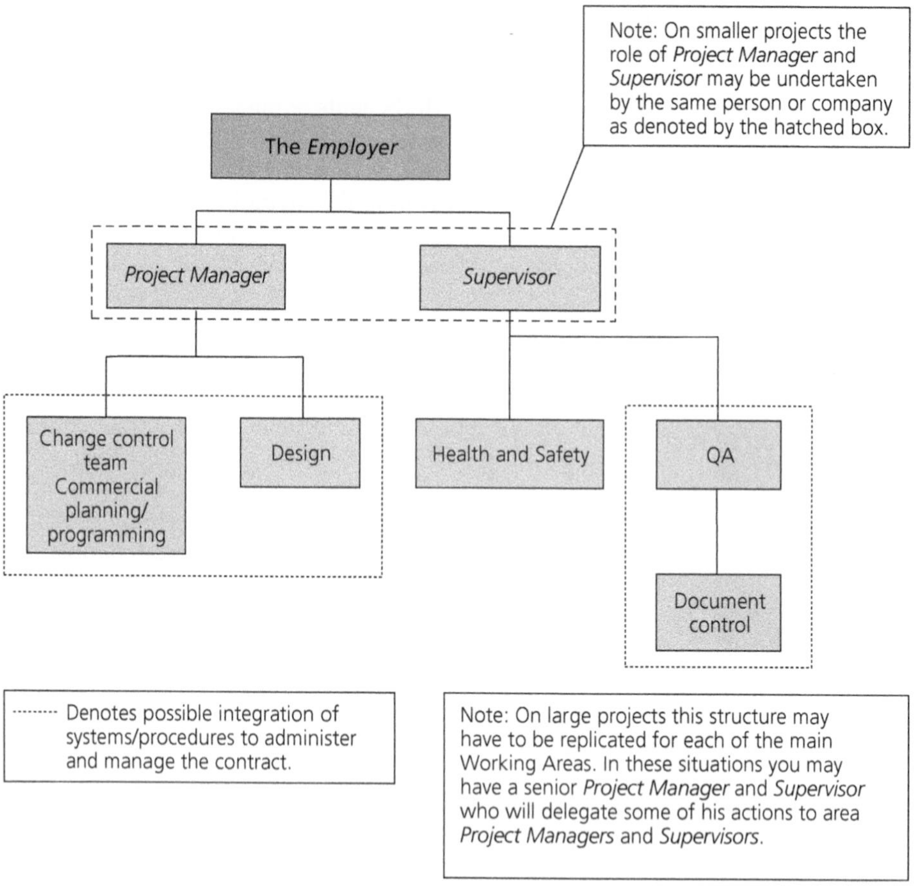

2.6.2 Integration of the project team

The ECC places considerable emphasis on the importance of working together. Cooperation and integration are essential both between the Parties under the contract and the various roles.

Figure 2.3 shows how the *Employer*'s team may be organised. The *Project Manager* and the *Supervisor* are the two named representatives of the *Employer* in the contract and therefore the other functions required fall under these two main roles. On small projects the role of *Project Manager* and *Supervisor* may be undertaken by the same individual or company; however, both roles must be undertaken separately.

Figure 2.3 also indicates that even in this structure consideration should be given to the systems/procedures that will be used to administer and manage the contract and that it will be beneficial to integrate or use compatible systems. A good example of this is planning and programming, where a standard recognised package would be used by both Parties. Even this may need to be fine-tuned to ensure that you have compatible versions of the same package, for example, version 3.

Also indicated is a change control team. This is a combination of the commercial and planning functions to manage change on the project. On ECC projects these two functions are so closely related that it is a natural progression of the management structure to combine these two functions into one. It could also be argued that the change control team should also include design.

The change control team would deal with

- agreement of financial and time effects of change
- acceptance of programme revisions
- assessment of time/cost effects of compensation events

- determining the validity of compensation events
- risk management
- interface management, for example, Other packages, utilities, Others working on site, obtaining other approvals
- insurance.

On target cost/cost reimbursable contracts you might need an audit/procurement team to carry out the following tasks

- auditing Defined Cost
- assessment of Disallowed Cost
- payment certificates
- procurement procedures for external sourced works/items, for example, subcontractors
- forecast of out-turn cost
- earned value analysis.

Practical experience on ECC projects has thrown up a number of organisational issues, some of which are as follows.

- The disciplined approach to management and the adherence to the time-scales can only be achieved by having the right resources available during the currency of the contract.
- Planning/programming capability is essential to the successful administration of an ECC project.
- There are likely to be peaks and troughs of activity with regard to compensation events. The organisational structure of the team needs to be such that you have the flexibility to react to such situations.
- Delegation of powers and authority to act are essential. The *Employer* must be confident of the key players' competencies, capabilities and cultural outlook.
- Change control is better managed through a combined commercial and programme department.

Joint training of the whole team could facilitate bringing the team together so that it operates as a team rather than a bunch of individuals with different goals and agendas. Part of the training could involve ensuring that the individual and team objectives coincide so that an incentive is provided to work as a team.

Communication of the project organisation document will assist in delineating everyone's role within the team so that clear lines of communication are established.

Other aspects to consider are as follows.

- Regular meetings such as progress meetings and risk reduction meetings.
- Working together on aspects of the contract such as compensation event quotations to avoid 'paper tennis', thereby decreasing the time taken to reach a conclusion and minimising the dissipation of the team's views. Facilitating the working together of the *Employer*, *Contractor*, quantity surveyor (if one is being used on the project) and planner so that the same goal is achieved by all parties.
- Agreeing management systems so that the management of the contract becomes smoother and more acceptable.

The foregoing commentary applies equally to the *Contractor* and Subcontractors. The *Contractor*'s team structure should strive to emulate that of the *Employer*. Figures 2.4 and 2.5 represent examples of an integrated management team.

Figures 2.4 and 2.5 show how an integrated team may be set up. They show that some of the roles and functions could be fulfilled by either the *Contractor* or *Employer*'s person. In such situations it is still very important to ensure that the lines of communication, authority and

Figure 2.4 Integrated team – example 1

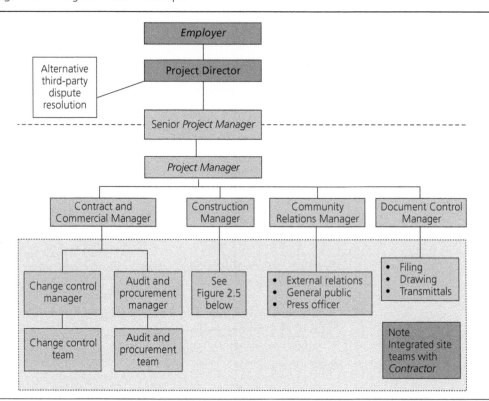

responsibility are clearly defined and allocated so that there is still an *Employer/Contractor* relationship in the event of issues or difficulties arising. Therefore the *Employer*'s agents the *Project Manager* and *Supervisor* still have a vital and important role to play in such team structures. You can see from these diagrams that on large projects there are many functions

Figure 2.5 Integrated team – example 2

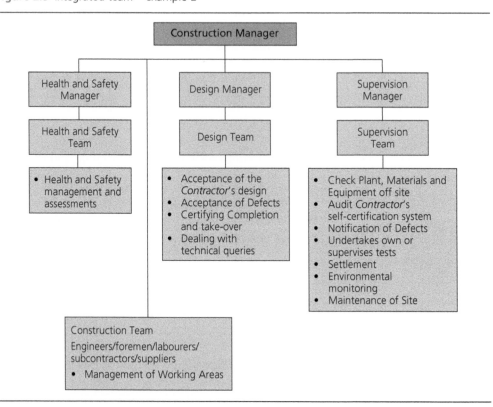

that are required to be undertaken, such as construction management and design. These functions are not discussed or recognised in the ECC. All of these roles are to be fulfilled through the *Project Manager* or the *Supervisor*.

A consequence of an integrated team or partnering, alliancing arrangement or even in the ECC in general is the need to consider the alignment of management and administrative procedures between the parties, for example, use of the same programming software, so that programme revisions can be easily communicated between the Parties.

Some clients have modified their contracts such that the actions under the contract are required by a new identified term *Project Team* rather than a *Project Manager*.

2.6.3 Monitoring the team

Continuous improvement remains central to the whole process and performance monitoring enables both parties to focus on challenges arising during the administration of a contract. The ECC lends itself to the production of Key Performance Indicators (KPIs), this providing no hiding place for poor performance.

The KPIs should be decided on at the beginning of the contract as well as the measurement of the KPIs and the regularity of the measurement. As with all measurements, they should be SMART (specific, measurable, achievable/aspirational, realistic and time bound). Examples of KPIs are as follows

- Client satisfaction
  - product
  - service.
- Quality (defects)
  - number
  - *Contractor* notified
  - speed of correction.
- Predictability
  - cost
  - time.

The secondary Partnering Option X12 includes in clause X12.4 information about incentives and KPIs.

KPIs are either included by choosing Option X12, the Partnering Option, or where X12 is not appropriate then Option X20 KPIs can be chosen. Secondary Options X12 and X20 are not to be used together.

> There is no hiding place – performance is highly visible.

2.7 What does the ECC mean to me?

The following items are merely snapshots of the impact of the ECC on the roles in the contract. The bullet points do not form the boundaries of the duties but rather the beginning.

2.7.1 To the whole project team?

The ECC is different from traditional contracts. The management of the contract is therefore also different.

- There is no hiding place – it is easy to produce KPIs and to highlight areas of non-performance.
- It is very demanding and requires action today not tomorrow.
- Adherence to strict time-scales is required.
- Setting up procedures and systems well in advance of the project commencing is recommended.
- There is an obligation on all parties to give an early warning of anything which may affect:
  - completion

- quality or
- cost of the works.
- On ECC contracts the management procedures apply equally to the *Contractor* and the consultant.
- Managing and allocating resources required can be difficult.
- Under Option B and D the *bill of quantities* is not Works Information.
- It should be evident from what has already been written in this book that the ECC requires a synchronisation of the relationships within a contract. The main *Contractor* can only provide good information if he is receiving good information from Subcontractors and the Subcontractors from their sub-subcontractors. This synchronisation will hopefully encourage collaborative arrangements.
- Mutual trust and cooperation underlie all actions.
- **You** make the project a success. Each individual has the power to contribute to or to contaminate the project and it is up to the team members to make the project a success.

2.7.2 To the *Project Manager*?

- Visible management skills are required.
- Set up procedures and systems well in advance of the project commencing.
- Set up a clearly defined team structure.
- Clear lines of communication.
- Delegation of powers.
- There is a need for a competent planner.
- In the instructions to tenderers put in an indicative *activity schedule*.
- Ensure that the tendered *activity schedule* is not front-loaded.
- Assess the amount due.
- Be fair and reasonable at all times.

2.7.3 To the designer?

The ECC document does not refer to the designer; however, a separate role for the *Employer*'s designer can be assumed. The function of the *Employer*'s designer is carried out through the *Project Manager*.

- It is essential that the *Employer*'s design element is complete at the time of tender with Option A and B.
- If using Option C it is important that the Works Information clearly states the design assumptions and any other criteria upon which the *Contractor* should base his price.
- It is essential that the Works Information is competently put together. It is at the heart of the ECC. It specifies and describes the *works* or states constraints on how the *works* are to be provided. It is important to note here that the Works Information is more than just a specification. Where the *Contractor* and the *Employer* both design parts of the *works*, the interfaces should be clearly stated.
- The standard of design liability for the *Employer*'s designer is reasonable skill and care.
- The design can have a big role to play in the success of the project in terms of cost, time and quality, and therefore management of the designer is essential.
- Poorly prepared Works Information will lead to what can be best termed 'latent compensation events', which under the contract may give rise to ambiguities and inconsistencies which may lead to compensation events.

> The quality of and completeness of the information provided by the designer is critical to the successful outcome of an ECC contract.

2.7.4 To the *Contractor*?

- Allocate somebody at the beginning of the contract to carry out a thorough review of the Works Information and Site Information with a view to fulfilling the *Contractor*'s obligations described in clauses 16.1 (early warning notifications), 17.1 (notification of ambiguities or inconsistencies between the contract documents) and 18.1 (notification of illegal and impossible requirements). Raise the appropriate notifications and forward to the *Project Manager*.

- Write to the *Project Manager* and ask him if, in accordance with clause 23, the *Project Manager* will be instructing the submission of the particulars of the design for any items of Equipment.
- Decide in good time what parts of the *works* are to be subcontracted and submit names of proposed Subcontractors in good time to the *Project Manager*. Note definition of Subcontractors is wider than the general understanding of term.
- Prepare the initial programme (if not submitted with the tender) within the period stated in the Contract Data and include all the information described in clause 31.2. Identify the critical path, time risk allowances and float. Preferably use one of the project management software packages to enable actual progress and the effects of compensation events/notified early warning matters to be shown. Submit revised programmes at the intervals stated in the Contract Data. Do not make the programme so detailed that it becomes unwieldy.
- At the beginning of the Contract write to the *Project Manager* asking him to decide when the first assessment date (for payment purposes) is, as described in clause 50.1.
- Secondary Option X15 limits the *Contractor*'s liability for the *Contractor*-designed work to reasonable skill and care. If Option X15 is not chosen, then the standard required is fitness for purpose.
- Negative compensation events – there may be occasions when work may be instructed to be omitted from a contract. It should be remembered that the prices inserted against the tendered *activity schedule* are not used to evaluate the effects of change. The effect of the change is measured as a compensation event, therefore the Schedule of Cost Components and the Fee is used to evaluate the change and the amount is removed from the total of the Prices.

If the *Contractor* has priced an item or activity too low, and it is then deleted from the contract, more money may be taken out of the contract than the *Contractor* had in for the work (because the Defined Cost as defined is greater than the price quoted initially).

- No payment is made to the *Contractor* for the cost of preparing compensation events for Options A and B.
- No payment is made for providing the *Project Manager* with a quotation for a proposed change to the *works* which is being considered for Options A and B.
- The *Contractor* does not have to notify the *Project Manager* of Completion; it is for the *Project Manager* to advise when Completion occurs.
- The *Contractor* does not have to submit applications for payment. It is the responsibility of the *Project Manager* to notify the *Contractor* of the amount due.
- The *Contractor* must advise the *Project Manager* within eight weeks of becoming aware of it that a compensation event has occurred. If the *Contractor* does not, then he will lose the contractual right to the compensation event. However, the contract makes it clear that if the compensation event should have been notified to the *Contractor* by the *Project Manager*, but was not, then the *Contractor* does not lose his entitlement to a change to the Prices, the Completion Date or a Key Date.
- Many quotations are based on forecast Defined Cost; these will contain an element of risk, for example, winter working.
- The *Contractor* is required to submit details of the effects on the programme of a compensation event, with every compensation event.
- The *Contractor* owns any terminal float on the programme. It is not there for the *Project Manager*'s use. The basis for the assessment of time is 'entitlement' and not 'need' as with other forms of contract.
- The sanction for not submitting an initial Accepted Programme is that 25% of the Price for Work Done to Date can be withheld. The *Project Manager* can make his own assessment of the effect of a compensation event in the absence of a programme. This may work against the *Contractor*. This can also put a heavy burden on the *Project Manager* if the *Contractor* does not perform.
- An *activity schedule* can be thought of as a contract sum analysis except that it is not used to evaluate the effects of change. Its sole use is as a payment schedule – a bit like a milestone schedule. The *Contractor* is only paid for completed activities in Option A.

- The *Contractor* needs to ensure that the Subcontractor is 'back to back' in terms of the following.
  - Providing information for compensation events, programme information, etc.
  - The Subcontractor's response *period for reply* being shorter than the response *period for reply* in the main contract. The best way to achieve this synchronisation with the Subcontractor is to use the NEC3 Engineering and Construction Subcontract.
  - The *Contractor*'s ensuring that all subcontracts include a statement that the parties to the contract will act in a spirit of trust and mutual cooperation.
  - Ensuring that amendments, special conditions of contract, special requirements, secondary Option Z clauses, Contract Data, Works Information, etc. are reflected in the subcontract.

> The ECC does not expect the *Contractor* to have a crystal ball to second guess what it is that the *Employer* wants.

2.7.5 To the *Supervisor*?

- Nearly all of the *Supervisor*'s actions are to be found in sections 4 and 7 of the *conditions of contract*.
- It is important that the *Supervisor* and the team below him are made aware of the importance of keeping good site diaries and records as there are occasions when compensation events will be based on historical costs.
- Ensure that you are familiar with the Works Information, especially testing, commissioning, etc.

2.7.6 To the *Employer*?

- Ensure that the *Project Manager* has the authority to act as required in the contract. Remember that the *Project Manager* has to act within stipulated time-scales.
- Ensure that your internal procedures do not hinder the role of the *Project Manager*.
- Ensure that your chosen *Project Manager* has the right skills and competencies and has the authority to act as required by the contract.
- Monitor the performance of your *Project Manager*, consider putting into place performance measurement or Key Performance Indicators, for example, response time to communications under the contract.

> It is essential that your *Project Manager* has the right skills and competencies and has the authority to act.

2.7.7 To the Subcontractor

The discussions in this book with regard to the *Contractor* apply equally to Subcontractors and their sub-subcontractors. One of the great benefits of the NEC suite of contracts is that the clauses in the ECC and ECC Subcontract follow the same pattern and there is a commonality of clauses.

You must ensure that you comply with the requirements of the NEC3 Subcontract and provide all the notices, programmes, quotations, etc. within the *period for reply*.

If you have your own subcontracts ensure that amendments, special conditions of contract, special requirements, secondary Option Z clauses, Contract Data, Works Information, etc. passed down by the *Contractor* are reflected in your subcontract.

> Good preparation is a key to the successful outcome of a contract. That means involving everyone not just the *Employer* and main *Contractor*.

2.8 Delegation

Both the *Project Manager* and the *Supervisor* may delegate any of their actions (clause 14.2), although preferably not to each other, and they can also cancel any delegation (clause 14.2). A delegation does not prevent the *Project Manager* or the *Supervisor* from carrying out that duty himself. Before any actions are delegated, the delegating party must first inform the *Contractor* of such delegation. It is also wise to notify for how long the delegation will be in place and also exactly what actions are being delegated.

The person to whom actions are delegated does not need to acquire a specific title under the contract, such as *Project Manager*'s Representative, since each individual will be the *Project Manager* for the actions they carry out, and similarly for the *Supervisor*.

> ■ Have all letters of delegation been issued?
> ■ Is everyone clear on their role and responsibilities?

2.9 Replacement of personnel

The *Employer* may replace the *Project Manager* or the *Supervisor* after notifying the *Contractor* of the name of the replacement (clause 14.4).

2.9.1 Removing people: clause 24.2

On reading clause 24.2 it can be easily interpreted that the *Contractor* should not have a day to remove the employee, but that removal should take place immediately. In fact, the clause does not rule out the latter action occurring. *Contractors* should note that this principle will apply to their own subcontracts.

The clause allows the following.

■ The *Project Manager* has the right to instruct the *Contractor* to remove any employee, which includes a Subcontractor's employees.
■ The *Project Manager* has to provide reasons to the *Contractor* for his instruction to remove an employee, but there is no restriction on those reasons (note that, in general, reasons will tend to pertain to health and safety), there is no obligation to behave reasonably and the action does not result in a compensation event.
■ The *Contractor* is required to arrange that, after one day, the employee has nothing further to do with the work.
■ The *Contractor* does not have one day to remove the employee, however. If the *Project Manager* requires the removal to be immediate, then the *Contractor* is obliged to obey the *Project Manager*. It may not always be reasonable to require immediate removal, however, particularly if the employee concerned is required to hand over documents or other information pertinent to the project.

Introduction to the Engineering and Construction Contract
ISBN 978-0-7277-5718-0

ICE Publishing: All rights reserved
doi: 10.1680/iecc.57180.049

Appendix 1
List of duties

Synopsis

This appendix describes the duties to be undertaken by each of the *Employer*, *Project Manager*, *Contractor* and *Supervisor* throughout the ECC.

A1.1   Core clauses

Clause	Contractor	Clause	Project Manager	Clause	Supervisor	Clause	Employer
10.1	To act as stated in the contract and in a spirit of mutual trust and cooperation	10.1	To act as stated in the contract and in a spirit of mutual trust and cooperation	10.1	To act as stated in the contract and in a spirit of mutual trust and cooperation	10.1	To act as stated in the contract and in a spirit of mutual trust and cooperation
13.1	To communicate in a form which can be read, copied and recorded	13.1	To communicate in a form which can be read, copied and recorded	13.1	To communicate in a form which can be read, copied and recorded	13.1	To communicate in a form which can be read, copied and recorded
13.3	To reply to a communication within the period for reply	13.3	To reply to a communication within the period for reply	13.3	To reply to a communication within the period for reply		
13.4	To resubmit a communication which is not accepted within the period for reply	13.4	To reply to a communication submitted or resubmitted for acceptance To state reasons for non-acceptance				
13.5	Agree/not agree to extension to period for reply	13.5	To notify any agreed extension to the period for reply				
		13.6	To issue certificates to the Employer and to the Contractor	13.6	To issue certificates to the Project Manager and to the Contractor		
13.7	To communicate notifications separately from other communications	13.7	To communicate notifications separately from other communications				
		13.8	May withhold acceptance of a submission by the Contractor				
		14.2	To notify the Contractor before delegating any actions or cancelling any delegation	14.2	To notify the Contractor before delegating any actions or cancelling any delegation		
		14.3	May give an instruction which changes the Works Information or a Key Date				
						14.4	To give notice to the Contractor before replacing the Project Manager or the Supervisor

Clause	Contractor	Clause	Project Manager	Clause	Supervisor	Clause	Employer
15.1	May submit a proposal for adding to the Working Areas to the *Project Manager* for acceptance	15.1	To reply to the *Contractor*'s proposal for adding to the Working Areas To state reasons for non-acceptance				
16.1	To give early warning of matters with delay, cost or performance implications or delay meeting a Key Date	16.1	To give early warning of matters with delay, cost or performance implications or delay meeting a Key Date To enter early warning matters in the Risk Register				
16.2	May give instruction to *Project Manager* to attend risk reduction meeting May instruct others to attend	16.2	May give instruction to *Contractor* to attend risk reduction meeting May instruct others to attend				
16.3	To cooperate at risk reduction meetings	16.3	To cooperate at risk reduction meetings				
		16.4	To record decisions made by revising the Risk Register and issuing to *Contractor* To instruct change to Works Information, if required, at the same time as issuing the revised Risk Register				
17.1	To give notice of ambiguities or inconsistencies in the documents	17.1	To give notice of ambiguities or inconsistencies in the documents To give instructions resolving ambiguities or inconsistencies				
18.1	To give notice of any illegality or impossibility in the Works Information	18.1	To give instructions changing the Works Information in the event of illegality or impossibility in the Works Information				
		19.1	To give an instruction dealing with an event described				
20.1	To Provide the Works in accordance with the Works Information						

Clause	Contractor	Clause	Project Manager	Clause	Supervisor	Clause	Employer
21.1	To design such parts of the works as stated in the Works Information						
21.2	To submit particulars of his design for acceptance as required by the Works Information	21.2	To accept particulars of the Contractor's design or to give reasons for non-acceptance				
23.1	To submit when instructed particulars of design of items of Equipment	23.1	To accept particulars of the design of Equipment or to give reasons for non-acceptance				
24.1	To employ key persons as stated in the Contract Data or acceptable replacements. To submit the name, qualifications and experience of proposed replacement person	24.1	To accept replacement persons proposed by the Contractor or to give reasons for non-acceptance				
24.2	To remove any employee on the Project Manager's instructions	24.2	May instruct the Contractor to remove an employee having stated his reasons				
25.1	To cooperate with Others in obtaining and providing information. To share the Working Areas with Others as stated in the Works Information						
25.2	To provide services and other things. To pay the cost assessed for not providing facilities and services	25.2	To assess the cost incurred if the Contractor does not provide the services and other things			25.2	To provide services and other things
25.3	To pay Employer's cost incurred if work does not meet a Condition for a Key Date	25.3	To assess the additional cost				
26.2	To submit the names of proposed Subcontractors for acceptance	26.2	To accept proposed Subcontractors or to give reasons for non-acceptance				

Clause	Contractor	Clause	Project Manager	Clause	Supervisor	Clause	Employer
	To appoint a Subcontractor only after the *Project Manager* has accepted him						
26.3	To submit the proposed conditions of contract for each subcontract for acceptance	26.3	To accept proposed subcontract conditions or to give reasons for non-acceptance				
	To appoint a Subcontractor on the proposed conditions of subcontract only after the *Project Manager* has accepted them						
27.1	To obtain approval of his own design from Others where necessary						
27.2	To provide access to the *works* to the *Project Manager*, *Supervisor* and Others						
27.3	To obey instructions given by the *Project Manager* or the *Supervisor* which are in accordance with the contract						
27.4	To act in accordance with health and safety regulations						
30.1	To start work on Site on or after the first *access date*						
	To do the work so that Completion is on or before the Completion Date						
		30.2	To decide the date of Completion				
			To certify Completion within one week of Completion				
30.3	To do the work so that the Condition stated for each Key Date is met by the Key Date						

Clause	Contractor	Clause	Project Manager	Clause	Supervisor	Clause	Employer
31.1	To submit a programme for acceptance within a period stated in the Contract Data						
31.2	To show details in each programme as listed						
		31.3	To accept the *Contractor's* programme within two weeks of submission or to give reasons for non-acceptance				
32.1	To show details in revised programmes as listed						
32.2	To submit a revised programme when instructed to or as required in the Contract Data	32.2 and 31.3	To accept a revised programme or to give reasons for non-acceptance				
						33.1	To give access of each part of the site before the later of the access date and the date for access shown on the Accepted Programme
		34.1	May instruct *Contractor* to stop or not start any work and later to re-start or start it				
						35.1	To take over the *works* not more than two weeks after Completion
						35.2	To take over any part of the *works* put into use (subject to exceptions)
		35.3	To certify within one week the date when the *Employer* takes over any part of the *works*				
		36.1	May instruct the *Contractor* to submit a quotation for acceleration				

Clause	Contractor	Clause	Project Manager	Clause	Supervisor	Clause	Employer
			To state changes to the Key Dates to be included in the quotation				
36.2	To submit a quotation for acceleration when so instructed or give reasons for not doing so						
40.2	To provide materials, facilities and samples for tests and inspections as stated in the Works Information					40.2	To provide materials, facilities and samples for tests and inspections as stated in the Works Information
40.3	To notify the Supervisor of tests and inspections before they start To notify the Supervisor of the results of tests and inspections To notify the Supervisor before doing work which would obstruct tests or inspections			40.3	To notify the Contractor of his tests and inspections before they start and afterwards of the results		
40.4	To correct Defects revealed by tests or inspections and to repeat such tests or inspections						
				40.5	To do tests and inspections without causing unnecessary delay to work or payment		
40.6	To pay the assessed cost incurred by the Employer in repeating tests or inspections	40.6	To assess the cost incurred by the Employer in repeating a test or inspection after a Defect is found				
41.1	To wait for notification from the Supervisor before bringing to the Working Areas those Plant and Materials that the Works Information states are to be inspected or tested before delivery			41.1	To notify the Contractor of the results of the test or inspection on Plant and Materials required by the Works Information to be tested or inspected before delivery		

Clause	Contractor	Clause	Project Manager	Clause	Supervisor	Clause	Employer
42.1	To carry out searches as instructed by the *Supervisor*			42.1	May instruct the *Contractor* to search for a Defect and to give reasons for searches which are instructed		
42.2	To notify the *Supervisor* of Defects found before the *defects date*			42.2	To notify the *Contractor* of Defects found before the *defects date*		
43.1	To correct Defects						
43.2	To correct notified defects before the end of the *defect correction period*						
				43.3	To issue the Defects Certificate at the later of the *defects date* and the last *defect correction period*		
		43.4	To arrange for the *Employer* to allow access and use to the *Contractor* of any part of the *works* needed for the correction of Defects after taking over			43.4	To allow access to the *Contractor* after takeover if needed for the correction of a Defect
44.1	May propose to *Project Manager* that Works Information should be changed to avoid correction of a Defect	44.1	May propose to *Contractor* that Works Information should be changed to avoid correction of a Defect				
44.2	To submit a quotation for reduced Prices or an earlier Completion Date or both	44.2	To change the Works Information, the Prices and the Completion Date if a quotation for not correcting Defects is accepted				
45.1	To pay the assessed costs of notified Defects being corrected by others because they were not corrected within the *defect correction period* even though access was given	45.1	To assess the cost of having Defects corrected by others if the *Contractor* fails to correct notified Defects within the *defect correction period* even though access was given				

Clause	Contractor	Clause	Project Manager	Clause	Supervisor	Clause	Employer
45.2	To pay cost assessed of correcting Defect where access not given	45.2	To assess the cost of correcting Defect where Contractor not given access to correct it				
		50.1	To assess the amount due for payment at each assessment date				
			To decide the first assessment date to suit the procedures of the parties				
		50.3	To retain one quarter of the Price for Work Done to Date until the Contractor has submitted a first programme showing information required				
50.4	May submit application for payment on or before the assessment date	50.4	To consider any application from the Contractor when assessing amounts due for payment				
			To give the Contractor details of how amounts due have been assessed				
		50.5	To correct any wrongly assessed amount due in a later payment certificate				
51.1	To pay the Employer if an interim assessment reduces the amount due from that already paid	51.1	To certify payment within one week of each assessment date			51.1	To pay amounts due to the Contractor
						51.2	To pay within three weeks of the assessment date
							To pay interest on late payment
		51.3	To assess interest to be paid on correcting amounts			51.3	To pay interest on correcting amounts

Clause	Contractor	Clause	Project Manager	Clause	Supervisor	Clause	Employer
61.1	To put instructions or changed decisions into effect	61.1	To notify the *Contractor* of compensation events which arise from the giving of instructions or changing of earlier decisions				
			To instruct the *Contractor* to submit quotations				
		61.2	May instruct the *Contractor* to submit quotations for a proposed instruction or proposed changed decision				
61.3	To give notice of a compensation event						
61.4	May notify the *Project Manager* if the *Project Manager* does not notify his decision to the *Contractor* within one week (or longer if agreed)	61.4	To decide within one week of notification (or such longer period as the *Contractor* agrees) whether the Prices, the Key Dates and the Completion Date should be changed when the *Contractor* notifies a compensation event				
			To notify the *Contractor* of the decision and instruct the *Contractor* to submit quotations				
		61.5	To decide whether the *Contractor* did not give any early warning of a compensation event which could have been given and to notify the *Contractor* of his decision				
		61.6	To state assumptions for the assessment of compensation events in the event that the effects are too uncertain to be forecast reasonably				
			To notify a correction to any assumptions later found to have been wrong				

Clause	Contractor	Clause	Project Manager	Clause	Supervisor	Clause	Employer
62.1	To discuss with the *Project Manager* different ways of dealing with the compensation event that are practicable To submit alternative quotations for compensation events if instructed to do so May submit quotations for other methods of dealing with the compensation event	62.1	To discuss with the *Contractor* different ways of dealing with the compensation event that are practicable May instruct the *Contractor* to submit alternative quotations				
62.2	To submit details of his assessment with each quotation To include alterations to the Accepted Programme with the quotation if the compensation event has altered the programme for the remaining work						
62.3	To submit quotations for compensation events within three weeks of being instructed to do so	62.3	To reply to quotations for compensation events within two weeks of the submission				
62.4	To submit revised quotations for compensation events within three weeks of being instructed to do so	62.4	To give reasons to the *Contractor* when instructing the submission of a revised quotation				
		62.5	To extend the time allowed for the submission of quotations and replies if the *Contractor* agrees To notify the *Contractor* of any agreed extensions for the submission of quotations or replies				
62.6	May notify the *Project Manager* if the *Project Manager* does not reply to a quotation within the time allowed To state which quotation is to be treated as having been accepted						

Clause	Contractor	Clause	Project Manager	Clause	Supervisor	Clause	Employer
63.5	To assess the event as if the *Contractor* had given an early warning if the *Project Manager* has notified the *Contractor* of his decision under clause 61.5	63.5	To assess the event as if the *Contractor* had given an early warning if the *Project Manager* has notified the *Contractor* of his decision under clause 61.5				
63.9	To take the correction into account when assessing the compensation event for the change to the Works Information	63.9	To correct the description of a condition for a Key Date if a change to the Works Information makes the description incorrect				
			To take the correction into account when assessing the compensation event for the change to the Works Information				
		64.1	To assess a compensation event: ■ if the *Contractor* has not submitted a quotation and details within the time allowed ■ if the *Project Manager* decides the *Contractor* has not assessed the compensation event correctly ■ if the *Contractor* has not submitted a required programme ■ if the *Project Manager* has not accepted the *Contractor*'s latest programme				
		64.2	To assess a compensation event using his own assessment of the programme: ■ if there is no Accepted Programme ■ if the *Contractor* has not submitted a revised/altered programme for acceptance as required				

Clause	Contractor	Clause	Project Manager	Clause	Supervisor	Clause	Employer
		64.3	To notify the *Contractor* of any assessments made (inclusive of details) of a compensation event within the period allowed to the *Contractor* for his quotation				
64.4	May notify the *Project Manager* if *Project Manager* did not assess a compensation event within the time allowed To state which quotation is to be treated as having been accepted						
		65.1	To implement compensation events notifying the *Contractor* of accepted quotations; or his own assessments; or a *Contractor*'s quotation treated as having been accepted by the *Project Manager*				
				71.1	To mark Equipment, Plant and Materials outside the Working Areas for payment purposes		
72.1	To remove Equipment from the Site when it is no longer needed						
73.1	To notify the finding of any object of value, historical or other interest Not to move the object without instructions	73.1	To instruct the *Contractor* how to deal with objects of value, historical or other interest				
81.1	To carry risks which are not the *Employer*'s risk from the *starting date* until the Defects Certificate is issued						

Clause	Contractor	Clause	Project Manager	Clause	Supervisor	Clause	Employer
82.1	To replace loss or repair damage to the *works*, Plant and Materials until the Defects Certificate is issued						
83.1	To indemnify the *Employer* against claims etc. due to *Contractor*'s risks					83.1	To indemnify the *Contractor* against claims etc. due to *Employer*'s risks
84.1	To provide insurances as required by the contract					84.1	To provide insurances as stated in the Contract Data
85.1	To submit insurance policies and certificates for acceptance as required by the contract	85.1	To accept policies and certificates of insurance submitted by the *Contractor* or to give reasons for non-acceptance				
85.3	To comply with the terms and conditions of insurance policies					85.3	To comply with the terms and conditions of insurance policies
86.1	To pay the costs incurred by the *Employer* in covering insurances which are the *Contractor*'s responsibility					86.1	May insure a risk which the *Contractor* should insure if the *Contractor* does not submit a required policy or certificate
87.1	To accept insurance policies and certificates provided by the *Employer* if they comply with the contract	87.1	To submit to the *Contractor* policies and certificates for insurances to be provided by the *Employer* as required by the contract			87.1	To provide policies and certificates for Insurances to the *Project Manager*
87.3	May insure a risk which the *Employer* should insure if the *Employer* does not submit a required policy or certificate					87.3	To pay the costs incurred by the *Contractor* in covering insurances which are the *Employer*'s responsibility
90.1	To notify the *Project Manager* and the *Employer*, giving details of reasons before terminating	90.1	To issue a termination certificate promptly when either Party gives notice of termination for reasons complying with the contract			90.1	To notify the *Project Manager* and the *Contractor*, giving details of reasons before terminating
		90.4	To certify final payment within 13 weeks of termination			90.4	To make payment within three weeks of the *Project Manager*'s certificate

Clause	Contractor	Clause	Project Manager	Clause	Supervisor	Clause	Employer
90.5	To do no further work to Provide the Works after the termination certificate has been issued						
						92.1	May complete works himself and may use Plant and Materials to which he has title
92.2	To leave the Working Areas and remove Equipment on termination To remove Equipment promptly from Site when Project Manager notifies him that Employer no longer needs it	92.2	To notify the Contractor that the Employer no longer needs Equipment to which the Contractor has title			92.2	May instruct the Contractor to leave the Site, remove any Equipment, Plant and Materials and assign subcontracts May use any Equipment to which the Contractor has title

A1.2   Main option clauses
A1.2.1   Option A

Clause	Contractor	Clause	Project Manager
31.4	To provide information which shows how each activity on the current *activity schedule* relates to the operations on each programme submitted for acceptance		
		36.3	To change the Completion Date, the Prices and the Key Dates when a quotation for acceleration is accepted and to accept the revised programme
54.2	If the *Contractor* changes a planned method of working at his discretion to submit revisions to the *activity schedule* so that it is compatible with the Accepted Programme	54.2	To accept revisions to the *activity schedule* or give reasons for non-acceptance
63.14	To assess a compensation event using rates or lump sums instead of Defined Cost if the *Project Manager* agrees	63.14	To assess a compensation event using rates or lump sums instead of Defined Cost if the *Contractor* agrees
65.4	To include changes to the Prices, the Completion Date and to Key Dates when notifying implementation of a compensation event	65.4	To include changes to the Prices, the Completion Date and to Key Dates when notifying implementation of a compensation event

A1.2.2 Option B

Clause	*Contractor*	Clause	*Project Manager*
		36.3	To change the Completion Date, the Prices and the Key Dates when a quotation for acceleration is accepted and to accept the revised programme
		60.6	To correct mistakes in the *bill of quantities* which are departures from the rules in the *method of measurement* or due to ambiguities or inconsistencies
63.13	To assess a compensation event using rates or lump sums instead of Defined Cost if the *Project Manager* agrees		
65.4	To include changes to the Prices, the Completion Date and to Key Dates when notifying implementation of a compensation event	65.4	To include changes to the Prices, the Completion Date and to Key Dates when notifying implementation of a compensation event

A1.2.3 Option C

Clause	Contractor	Clause	Project Manager
20.3	To advise the Project Manager on the practical implications of the design of the works and on the subcontracting arrangements		
20.4	To prepare forecasts of the total Defined Cost for the whole of the works and submit them to the Project Manager	20.4	To consult with the Contractor on the preparation of forecasts of total Defined Costs
26.4	To submit the proposed contract data for each subcontract for acceptance	26.4	To accept proposed contract data for subcontracts or to give reasons for non-acceptance
31.4	To provide information which shows how each activity on the current activity schedule relates to the operations on each programme submitted for acceptance		
		36.3	To change the Completion Date, the Prices and the Key Dates when a quotation for acceleration is accepted and to accept the revised programme
		40.7	To not include amounts due to the Contractor for the cost of carrying out the repeat test or inspection
52.2	To keep the described records of costs and payments		
52.3	To allow the Project Manager to inspect accounts and records		
		53.1	To assess the Contractor's share of the difference between the total of the Prices and the Price for Work Done to Date

Clause	Contractor	Clause	Project Manager
		53.3	To make a preliminary assessment of the *Contractor's* share at Completion
		53.4	To assess the *Contractor's* share in the final amount due using the final Price for Work Done to Date and the final total of the Prices
54.2	To submit a revision to the *activity schedule* if the *Contractor* changes a planned method of working	54.2	To accept a revision to the *activity schedule* or to give reasons for non-acceptance
63.15	To assess a compensation event using the Shorter Schedule of Cost Components if the *Project Manager* agrees	63.15	May make his own assessments using the Shorter Schedule of Cost Components
65.4	To include changes to the Prices, the Completion Date and to Key Dates when notifying implementation of a compensation event	65.4	To include changes to the Prices, the Completion Date and to Key Dates when notifying implementation of a compensation event
		93.4	To assess the *Contractor's* share after certifying termination

A1.2.4   Option D

Clause	Contractor	Clause	Project Manager
20.3	To advise the *Project Manager* on the practical implications of the design of the *works* and on the subcontracting arrangements		
20.4	To prepare forecasts of the total Defined Cost for the whole of the *works* and submit them to the *Project Manager*	20.4	To consult with the *Contractor* on the preparation of forecasts of total Defined Costs
26.4	To submit the proposed contract data for each subcontract for acceptance	26.4	To accept proposed contract data for subcontracts or to give reasons for non-acceptance
		36.3	To change the Completion Date, the Prices and the Key Dates when a quotation for acceleration is accepted and to accept the revised programme
		40.7	To not include amounts due to the *Contractor* for the cost of carrying out the repeat test or inspection
52.2	To keep the described records of costs and payments		
52.3	To allow the *Project Manager* to inspect accounts and records		
		53.5	To assess the *Contractor*'s share of the difference between the Total of the Prices and the Price for Work Done to Date
		53.7	To make a preliminary assessment of the *Contractor*'s share at Completion

Clause	Contractor	Clause	Project Manager
		53.8	To assess the *Contractor*'s share in the final amount due using the final Price for Work Done to Date and the final Total of the Prices
		60.6	To correct mistakes in the *bill of quantities* which are departures from the rules in the *method of measurement* or due to ambiguities or inconsistencies
63.15	To assess a compensation event using the Shorter Schedule of Cost Components if the *Project Manager* agrees	63.15	May make his own assessments using the Shorter Schedule of Cost Components
63.13	To assess a compensation event using rates or lump sums if the *Project Manager* agrees		
65.4	To include changes to the Prices, the Completion Date and to Key Dates when notifying implementation of a compensation event	65.4	To include changes to the Prices, the Completion Date and to Key Dates when notifying implementation of a compensation event
		93.5	To assess the *Contractor*'s share after certifying termination

A1.2.5 Option E

Clause	Contractor	Clause	Project Manager
20.3	To advise the *Project Manager* on the practical implications of the design of the work and on the subcontracting arrangements		
20.4	To prepare forecasts of the total Defined Cost for the whole of the *works* and submit them to the *Project Manager*	20.4	To consult with the *Contractor* on the preparation of forecasts of total Defined Cost
26.4	To submit the proposed contract data for each subcontract for acceptance	26.4	To accept proposed contract data for subcontracts or to give reasons for non-acceptance
		36.4	To change the Completion Date, the Key Dates and the forecast of the total Defined Cost of the whole of the *works* when a quotation for acceleration is accepted and to accept the revised programme
52.2	To keep the described records of costs and payments		
52.3	To allow the *Project Manager* to inspect accounts and records		
63.15	To assess a compensation event using the Shorter Schedule of Cost Components if the *Project Manager* agrees	63.15	May make his own assessments using the Shorter Schedule of Cost Components
65.3	To include changes to the forecast amount of the Prices, the Completion Date and the Key Dates in the notification implementing a compensation event	65.3	To include changes to the forecast amount of the Prices, the Completion Date and the Key Dates in the notification implementing a compensation event

A1.2.6 Option F

Clause	*Contractor*	Clause	*Project Manager*
20.2	To manage the *Contractor*'s design, the provision of the Site services and the construction and installation of the *works*		
	To subcontract the *Contractor*'s design, the provision of the Site services and the construction and installation of the *works* except work which the Contract Data states he will do himself		
20.3	To advise the *Project Manager* on the practical implications of the design of the *works* and on subcontracting arrangements		
20.4	To prepare forecasts of the total Defined Cost for the whole of the *works* in conjunction with the *Project Manager* and to submit them to the *Project Manager*	20.4	To consult with the *Contractor* on the preparation of forecasts of total Defined Costs
20.5	To agree the change to the price for the work and any change to the Key Dates and Completion Date if the work the *Contractor* is to do himself is affected by a compensation event	20.5	To agree the change to the price for the work and any change to the Key Dates and Completion Date if the work the *Contractor* is to do himself is affected by a compensation event
			To decide the change if the *Contractor* and the *Project Manager* cannot agree
26.4	To submit the proposed contract data for each subcontract for acceptance	26.4	To accept proposed contract data for subcontracts or to give reasons for non-acceptance

Clause	Contractor	Clause	Project Manager
		36.4	To change the Completion Date, the Key Dates and the forecast of the total defined Cost of the whole of the *works* when a quotation for acceleration is accepted and to accept the revised programme
52.2	To keep the described records of costs and payments		
52.3	To allow the *Project Manager* to inspect accounts and records		
65.3	To include changes to the forecast amount of the Prices, the Completion Date and the Key Dates in the notification implementing a compensation event	65.3	To include changes to the forecast amount of the Prices, the Completion Date and the Key Dates in the notification implementing a compensation event

A1.3 Dispute resolution procedure option clauses
A1.3.1 Option W1 – to be used except in the UK when the Housing Grants, Construction and Regeneration Act 1996 applies

Clause	Contractor	Clause	Project Manager	Clause	Adjudicator	Clause	Employer
				W1.1	To decide any dispute referred to him		
W1.2(1)	To appoint the *Adjudicator* under the NEC3 Adjudicator's Contract current at the *starting date*					W1.2(1)	To appoint the *Adjudicator* under the NEC3 Adjudicator's Contract current at the *starting date*
				W1.2(2)	To act impartially and decide the dispute as an independent adjudicator and not as arbitrator		
W1.2(3)	To choose an adjudicator jointly or ask the *Adjudicator nominating body* to choose an adjudicator if the *Adjudicator* is not identified in the Contract Data or resigns or is unable to act					W1.2(3)	To choose an adjudicator jointly or ask the *Adjudicator nominating body* to choose an adjudicator if the *Adjudicator* is not identified in the Contract Data or resigns or is unable to act
				W1.2(4)	The replacement *Adjudicator* decides the dispute		
				W1.2(5)	To not be liable to the Parties for any action or failure to take action unless in bad faith		
W1.3(1)	May refer a dispute about an action of the *Project Manager* or the *Supervisor*; or the *Project Manager* or the *Supervisor* not having taken an action May refer any other matter					W1.3(1)	May refer a dispute about a quotation for a compensation event which is treated as having been accepted May refer any other matter

Clause	Contractor	Clause	Project Manager	Clause	Adjudicator	Clause	Employer
		W1.3(2)	May extend times for notifying and referring a dispute				
W1.3(4)	May refer a subcontract dispute at the same time as the main contract referral						
				W1.3(5)	May review and revise actions, ascertain facts, request a party to submit more information, issue instructions required to reach his decision		
				W1.3(7)	To make assessments in the same way as a compensation event		
				W1.3(8)	To decide the dispute by notifying the Parties and the *Project Manager*		
W1.3(9)	To proceed as if the matter disputed were not disputed	W1.3(9)	To proceed as if the matter disputed were not disputed			W1.3(9)	To proceed as if the matter disputed were not disputed
W1.4(1)	To not refer any dispute to the *tribunal* unless it has been referred to the *Adjudicator*		(The *Supervisor* also has a duty to proceed as if the matter were not disputed)			W1.4(1)	To not refer any dispute to the *tribunal* unless it has been referred to the *Adjudicator*

A1.3.2 Option W2 – to be used in the UK when the Housing Grants, Construction and Regeneration Act 1996 applies (incorporating amendments of September 2011)

Clause	Contractor	Clause	Project Manager	Clause	Adjudicator	Clause	Employer
W2.1(1)	May refer a dispute at any time to the *Adjudicator*			W2.1(1)	To decide any dispute referred to him	W2.1(1)	May refer a dispute at any time to the *Adjudicator*
W2.2(1)	To appoint the *Adjudicator* under the NEC3 Adjudicator's Contract current at the *starting date*					W2.2(1)	To appoint the *Adjudicator* under the NEC3 Adjudicator's Contract current at the *starting date*
				W2.2(2)	To act impartially and decide the dispute as an independent adjudicator and not as arbitrator		
W2.2(3)	To choose an adjudicator jointly or ask the *Adjudicator nominating body* to choose an adjudicator if the *Adjudicator* is not identified in the Contract Data or resigns or is unable to act					W2.2(3)	To choose an adjudicator jointly or ask the *Adjudicator nominating body* to choose an adjudicator if the *Adjudicator* is not identified in the Contract Data or resigns or is unable to act
				W2.2(4)	The replacement *Adjudicator* decides the dispute		
				W2.2(5)	To not be liable to the Parties for any action or failure to take action unless in bad faith		
W2.3(1)	To give notice of the adjudication to the *Employer* before referring a dispute to the *Adjudicator*			W2.3(1)	To notify the Parties whether he is able to decide the dispute	W2.3(1)	To give notice of the adjudication to the *Contractor* before referring a dispute to the *Adjudicator*
W2.3(3)	May refer a subcontract dispute at the same time as the main contract referral						

Clause	Contractor	Clause	Project Manager	Clause	Adjudicator	Clause	Employer
				W2.3(4)	May review and revise actions, ascertain facts, request a party to submit more information, issue instructions required to reach his decision		
				W2.3(7)	To make assessments in the same way as a compensation event		
				W2.3(8)	To decide the dispute by notifying the Parties and the *Project Manager* May allocate fees and expenses between the Parties		
W2.3(9)	To proceed as if the matter disputed were not disputed	W2.3(9)	To proceed as if the matter disputed were not disputed			W2.3(9)	To proceed as if the matter disputed were not disputed
W2.4(1)	To not refer any dispute to the *tribunal* unless it has been referred to the *Adjudicator*					W2.4(1)	To not refer any dispute to the *tribunal* unless it has been referred to the *Adjudicator*

A1.4   Secondary option clauses
A1.4.1   Option X4 – Parent company guarantee

Clause	Contractor	Clause	Project Manager
X4.1	To give the *Employer* a parent company guarantee in a form set out in the Works Information		

A1.4.2 Option X7 – Delay damages

Clause	Contractor	Clause	Project Manager	Clause	Supervisor	Clause	Employer
X7.1	To pay delay damages as stated in the Contract Data from the Completion Date until Completion or take over						
						X7.2	To repay any overpayment of delay damages with interest
		X7.3	To assess the benefit to the *Employer* of taking over part of the *works* before Completion as a proportion of taking over all the *works* not previously taken over				

A1.4.3 Option X12 – Partnering

There are various actions on the Partners and the Core Group. Since these are defined, they cannot at this stage be allocated as the *Employer* and the *Contractor*. If they were to be, however, there are actions on the *Client*, the Partners and the Core Group.

A1.4.4 Option X13 – Performance bond

Clause	Contractor	Clause	Project Manager
X13.1	To give the *Employer* a performance bond for the amount stated in the Contract Data and in the form set out in the Works Information	X13.1	To accept the *Contractor's* performance bond or to give reasons for non-acceptance

A1.4.5 Option X14 – Advanced payment to the *Contractor*

Clause	*Contractor*	Clause	*Project Manager*	Clause	*Supervisor*	Clause	*Employer*
						X14.1	To make the advanced payment of the amount stated in the Contract Data
		X14.2	To accept an advanced payment bond or to give reasons for non-acceptance			X14.2	To make the advanced payment within four weeks of the Contract Date or receipt of the advanced payment bond
X14.3	To repay advanced payments to the *Employer* in instalments as stated in the Contract Data						

A1.4.6 Option X16 – Retention

Clause	*Contractor*	Clause	*Project Manager*
		X16.2	To halve the amount retained in the assessment made at Completion of the whole of the *works* or in the next assessment made after the *Employer* has taken over the whole of the *works* if this is before Completion of the whole of the *works* To retain nothing after the Defects Certificate has been issued

A1.4.7 Option X17 – Low performance damages

Clause	*Contractor*
X17.1	To pay low performance damages as stated in the Contract Data for Defects included in the Defects Certificate showing low performance

A1.4.8 Option X18 – Limitation of liability

Clause	Contractor
X18.5	To not be liable to the *Employer* for any matter to do with the contract which is notified to the *Contractor* after the *end of liability date*

A1.4.9 Option X20 – Key Performance Indicators (not used with Option X12)

Clause	Contractor	Clause	Project Manager	Clause	Employer
X20.2	To report to the *Project Manager* from the *starting date* until the Defects Certificate has been issued his performance against each Key Performance Indicator at the intervals stated in the Contract Data				
X20.3	To submit to the *Project Manager* his proposals for improving performance if his forecast final measurement against a Key Performance Indicator will not achieve the target stated in the Incentive Schedule				
				X20.5	May add a Key Performance Indicator and associated payment to the Incentive Schedule but he may not delete or reduce a payment stated in the Incentive Schedule

A1.4.10 Option Y(UK)2 – The Housing Grants, Construction and Regeneration Act 1996 (incorporating amendments of September 2011)

Clause	Contractor	Clause	Project Manager	Clause	Employer
		Y2.2	Issue certificate to the *Contractor* specifying the amount due at the payment due date (the notified sum) and stating the basis on which the amount was calculated		
Y2.3	To notify the other Party not later than seven days before the final date for payment by stating the amount considered to be due and the basis on which that sum is calculated as notification that payment of less than the notified sum is intended			Y2.3	To notify the other Party not later than seven days before the final date for payment by stating the amount considered to be due and the basis on which that sum is calculated as notification that payment of less than the notified sum is intended

Introduction to the Engineering and Construction Contract
ISBN 978-0-7277-5718-0

ICE Publishing: All rights reserved
doi: 10.1680/iecc.57180.081

Index